Word Games
for
Play and Power

Word Games
for
Play and Power

by
Joseph T. Shipley

PRENTICE-HALL, INC.
ENGLEWOOD CLIFFS, N.J.

Library of Congress Catalog Card Number: 62–11890

Printed in the United States of America

96422–T

To

Lesem Bach

in fellowship through half a century

Contents

Introduction

Words should be fun. The fun is fundamental. When you have to work hard to make words work for you, something is wrong.

You should enjoy words, play with them, make them familiar. Then they will respond to you, and let you command them. And the right word will come for your need.

The difference between the right word and the almost right word, as Mark Twain said, is the difference between the lightning and the lightning bug.

Not only "lightning" but enlightening. An apt turn of phrase may bring an enlightening flash.

I was present one night when my nephew and his wife took up the endless discussion of the training of their boy. The lad was now twelve, and his father thought he should be trusted to make some of his own decisions. He said to his wife:

"You're coddling him!"

"How can you say that!" she exclaimed. "It's natural to want to guide him. It's mother love."

"You've described it exactly," he said. "Smother-love."

The sudden turn of words checked her emotion, shocked her into thought. After that, the boy enjoyed a little more freedom.

Every day you have opportunities to "win friends and influence people" through the effective use of words.

A cynical phrase tells us that familiarity breeds contempt. It is as likely to breed contemplation. When words are familiar, their proper use becomes a habit, as simple as putting forward the legs in the right order when you walk. Walking and talking can both be learned. Your words should be good to stand on.

The best way to learn is by playing. Play puts into one package both interest and practice. Children and adults alike learn best through play.

The most recent method of teaching English to adult foreigners works with games. It has been presented by I. A. Richards with prefaces in forty-one languages, from Arabic through Czech, Sinhalese and Tagalog to Vietnamese. Lessons are turned into play.

Three varieties of simple games are used for the learners. They are so simple that you can make more like them yourself, easy enough for little tots, or hard enough to engage those that are expert with words.

A. The first game omits letters in the words of a sentence. From the letters given and the rest of the sentence, one must guess the word and put in the missing letters.

> 1. A d – – tion – – y is l – – ng on the desk.
> 2. The a – – pl – – e is about to l – – d.

B. The letters of words in a sentence are scrambled.

> 1. Fire gives us thae and thilg.
> 2. She tried on one dress after hotrane.

C. All the words of a sentence are given, but not in the correct order. They are to be unscrambled.

> 1. The world across is highest the from building the us street in.
> 2. A watchdogs than is friendly two better neighbor.

These, as you can see, are all quite simple. The answers are:

A. 1. dictionary, lying. 2. airplane, land. B. 1. heat, light. 2. another. C. 1. Across the street from us is the highest building in the world. 2. A friendly neighbor is better than two watchdogs.

Others can be made as difficult as desired. Here are two more scrambles:

1. The a world by future is ourselves limited.
2. The anguish one of of world beauty two edges of one has laughter.

Rearrange these to read: 1. The Future is a world limited by ourselves. 2. The world of beauty has two edges, one of anguish, one of laughter.

The world of words is unlimited. Its treasures are best approached along the roads of laughter.

There are many games in this book. Its purpose is not merely to give games, however, but to show how they work, how you can make more of them—and how through play you can build up avenues and resources of power.

1

Meanings

Let us look first at the growth of words. By slight shifts of meaning, a word may through generations take a long journey.

Many a word has turned a somersault in its history. *Silly* once meant *blessed*. *Boor* once meant *farmer*. *Pagan* meant *a dweller in the fields*. *Clumsy* meant *numb with cold*. *Lewd* meant *not a cleric,* and a *miscreant* was merely an *unbeliever*. The dove is named from its dipping its head as though diving. The Greek word for dove, *columbos,* also meant diver. Ask Christopher.

Pluck is a word that shows both recent change and long tradition. It means, of course, courage. A hundred years ago, however, the dictionaries recorded no such sense. Then they listed "the" pluck, the liver and lights of an animal, the part of a fowl the farmer would put his hand in and pluck out. First in boxing slang about 1780 the other sense appeared, then gradually it worked its way into the common speech. After a time, *pluck* became the commonplace word for stalwart courage, and sports writers and slangsters began to seek fresher words for a plucky fighter. Where did they go? Right back into the viscera: "That guy's got guts!"

The Bible speaks of the bowels of compassion, and observes, of a man obviously deficient in guts, "His bowels were loosed with fear." Thomas Benton has made a painting illustrating the

1

story of the Negro servant, sent by his master to get water from a pool near where they were encamped, hurrying back almost white with fear.

"What's the matter?"

"There's a crocodile in that water!"

"Oh, go on back there! He won't hurt you."

"I ain't heard *him* say that!"

"Why, that crocodile's just as frightened as you are."

"Well, if that crocodile's as scared as I am, that water ain't fit to drink!"

Plus ça change, plus c'est la même chose.

An early English prayer ran: "O Lord, prevent me in all my doings!" Prevent meant to come before; the Lord was to arrive first and prepare the way. But in our more sordid daily doings, if another man came before, he was likely to claim the prize for himself, and prevent—in the now current sense—others from attaining it.

The large size, unabridged *Oxford English Dictionary* lists all the present and past uses of the words it gives, together with illustrative quotations. Thus for the word *make,* it has 38 columns, 13 large pages.

When we say "The fat's in the fire!" few persons listen for the sizzle. More are likely to pull in their waistline when we speak of a fat woman, though not when we mention that all mammals, beneath the epidermis, have a layer of fat. You have a fat chance of getting all these ideas into one definition!

C.K. Ogden lists thirty current uses of the word living. That's living indeed!

The Oxford Dictionary gives the complete history, with illustrative examples, of 414,825 words. *Webster's New International Dictionary,* without examples, gives the meanings of 604,000 words.

MEANS

What a word means is frequently more important than it is obvious. Sometimes knowledge of the sense of a prefix con-

founds. You may figure that *in* at the beginning of a word means
into. But it may also (like *un-*) mean not, as *un*fit, *in*calculable.
And it may also be used to give strength to an idea. This is the
opposite of the negative use. For example, inflammable does not
mean unburnable; it is an intensive, or stronger, form of flammable. The confusion of the intensive *in* with the negative, however, has been so great that trucks carrying inflammable liquids
now bear the label FLAMMABLE.

Watch some variety, for a moment, from the Greek. In cenobite, the *ceno-* means in common; a cenobite is one that lives in
a community, the opposite of an anchorite. In cenozoic, the *ceno-*
means new; the cenozoic period of the world is the most recent,
covering only the last 60 odd million years. In cenotaph, the
ceno- means empty; a cenotaph is a memorial, an empty tomb.

Or ponder the flow of the Jordan, "the one wide river to cross"
to the Holy Land. As a word, the name survives in the Jordan
almond. Several meanings, however, more closely associated
with the river, have been forgotten.

1. Jordan meant a bottle. This was a shortening from Jordan-
bottle, a flask for carrying water from the holy river, as is still
done from the Ganges in India. I have met an elderly woman,
living several hundred miles from the river, who has never drunk
any water except that borne to her in a Ganges-bottle.

2. The jordan (bottle), probably with a long neck to prevent
spilling, came to be used by alchemists, then by early physicians
and astrologers for examining urine. By Shakespeare's time
(1 "Henry IV," II i 19–21; 2 "Henry IV," II iv 33), it had
descended in use to the lowly chamber-pot. In this sense, the jordan has largely been supplanted by the john.

3. From the figurative association of a pot and a head, the
jordan came to mean a noddle, a fool.

4. The meaning, a staff, or a blow with a staff ("I gave him
a jordan!") comes from another winding of the river into the
Scriptures, when Jacob said to the Lord: "With my staff I passed
over this Jordan."

The river Jordan keeps its separate identity through the whole length of the Sea of Galilee, but gets lost in the depressed and heavily saline waters of the Dead Sea. And of its meanings all that remains is a nut. But—ironically enough—the Jordan almond is not named after the river itself. It was originally called the jardin (French for garden) almond, a cultivated variety.

MATCH

The simplest meaning game, MATCH, provides a list of words, with a scrambled list of definitions. Dictate the words. Then dictate the meanings. Allow time for the players to match each word with its correct meaning. The first one to do this wins.

In the examples below, each meaning is followed by the number of the word to which it belongs. Easier or harder words can be chosen by anyone arranging a game of MATCH. Use a dictionary, and choose words to fit the players.

1. assuage	unsuitable; clumsy 10
2. actuate	very greedy 8
3. acrimonious	pacify 1
4. truncate	cautious; shy 5
5. chary	ceremonial procession; retinue 7
6. paragon	gesture of respect; deep bow 12
7. cortege	cut off a part 4
8. voracious	baffling puzzle or person 11
9. veracious	impel to action 2
10. inept	sharp-tempered, caustic 3
11. enigma	model of excellence 6
12. obeisance	honest 9

1. arroyo	natural inclination 2
2. proclivity	grim and horrible; ghastly 9
3. vapid	stubborn; hardhearted 7
4. autarchy	throw overboard; throw away 12
5. adroit	a dry gully; a stream 1
6. latent	skilful; clever 5
7. obdurate	enlarge; become greater 8
8. augment	absolute rule; country under a despot 4
9. macabre	damage 11

10. vacillate   uninteresting; dull 3
11. lesion   waver; be undecided 10
12. jettison   hidden; as yet unrevealed 6

Variation

Dictate ten words, without any definitions. Allow time for players to write the meanings. Each player reads one word and its definition. All check. Player with most right wins.

Here is a list of rather difficult words, without their meanings. Try them yourself, then on your friends. Or check the meanings in any unabridged dictionary, and scramble them for a game of MATCH.

1. coalesce 2. decant 3. descant 4. eudemonics 5. rennet
6. vagary 7. eupnea 8. tortuous 9. estovers 10. euphroe
11. fiasco 12. stipend 13. imminence 14. immanence
15. carboy 16. felucca 17. feretory 18. ferine 19. feculent
20. bezique 21. aspectabund 22. prostasy 23. saprophagous
24. chirapsy 25. terebinth 26. tawpy 27. dilatory 28. dilatatory 29. gazebo 30. exorn 31. pecten 32. sorites 33. aglet
34. agape (three syllables) 35. arcana 36. chryselephantine
37. diplomatics 38. feckless 39. feme 40. fennec 41. thymogenic 42. tribometer 43. ursine 44. viripotent 45. quidnunc
46. polypragmon 47. funis 48. clepsydra 49. chrisom
50. gestic 51. funipotent 52. chrestomathy 53. ptilosis
54. burgonet 55. thereologist 56. thelemite 57. cecutiency
58. theat 59. remex 60. terebra 61. hadiwist 62. plerophy
63. andabation (the common lot) 64. proglottid 65. enchorial
66. putamen 67. serendipity 68. palmary 69. adscititious
70. scree 71. purfle 72. friable 73. minacious 74. agrostology 75. manyplies 76. algidity 77. ancipitate 78. enantiomorph 79. euonymus 80. eulogia

LOOK AHEAD

The ancients never tired of trying to see the future. Perhaps it's as well that they could not succeed. Their attempts included hundreds of methods; most of these we label with a word ending in *-mancy*. GAME: Dictate ten ways of trying to peer into the days to come. Players write the method they think the word names. Player with most right wins.

Here are a few of the future words, with their meanings:

1. chiromancy 2. onychomancy 3. ceromancy 4. necromancy
5. lecanomancy 6. ophidomancy 7. spodomancy 8. astragalomancy 9. daphnomancy 10. tephramancy 11. uromancy
12. arithmancy 13. onomancy 14. gastromancy 15. gyromancy 16. enoptromancy 17. oenomancy 18. pedomancy
19. pyromancy 20. agnomancy 21. hippomancy 22. elaphomancy 23. entomancy 24. scolexomancy 25. osteomancy
26. craniomancy 27. genomancy 28. odontomancy 29. pteromancy 30. omphalomancy 31. iridomancy 32. limomancy
33. lygomancy 34. rhombomancy 35. teratomancy 36. thuromancy 37. cholomancy 38. clonomancy 39. crotalomancy
40. cymomancy 41. dapomancy 42. drosomancy 43. edeomancy 44. elaiomancy 45. epomancy 46. hagiomancy
47. amnimancy 48. aspidomancy 49. aureomancy 50. carpomancy

1. By reading the hand (lines, moisture, scars, dirt, etc.) 2. by nails reflecting the sun 3. by drippings of wax 4. by communion with the dead (This is the basic word for black magic.)
5. by inspection of a basin of water 6. by serpents 7. by ashes
8. with ankle bones. The astragals, which were primitive dice, could fall on two sides only. One of these was usually marked NIKE, the Greek word for Victory 9. with the laurel leaf
10. by tracings in ashes 11. by urine 12. by numbers 13. by the letters of one's name 14. with ventriloquism 15. by spinning in a circle. This device is preserved in children's games that spin one around thrice before one makes one's choice. 16. with one mirror 17. by color, sediment, or other peculiarities of wine
18. by the soles of the feet 19. by flickering flames 20. by a lamb 21. by giving a horse loose rein 22. by a deer 23. by insects 24. by worms 25. by bones 26. by an enemy's skull
27. by the jaw (bone) 28. by the teeth 29. by wings 30. by the navel 31. by the rainbow 32. by shapes discerned in mud
33. with hollow twigs (reeds) 34. by spinning (as of a top or coin) 35. by prodigies 36. by incense 37. by the bile 38. by broken branches 39. by dancing rhythm 40. by waves on a

beach   41. by the leavings at a feast   42. by the dew   43. by the
genitals   44. by pouring oil   45. by random words. A common
variety of this is bibliomancy: opening a book (especially
Homer, Virgil, or a Bible) and putting a finger down at random.
46. with sacred relics   47. by objects in a stream   48. by a shield
49. with gold (a favorite method!)   50. by fruitskins

PICK

The most frequent Meaning Game, because it is played on
college entrance and other examinations, is PICK. In this, a base
word is followed by four or five putative definitions, among
which the most nearly correct must be selected. Here are two
such sets:

1. inamissible—a. unapproachable   b. unacceptable   c. not
   likely to be lost   d. not to be conquered
2. inadulable—a. not to be flattered   b. not to be debased
   c. not to be increased   d. not to be altered
3. jactitation—a. playing dice   b. bragging   c. prophesying
   d. obscene gesturing
4. pogoniate—a. prone to argument   b. prone   c. bearded
   d. astute
5. sayid—a. motto   b. chief   c. remote   d. dreary
6. crocodilite—a. waterside flower   b. treachery   c. ancient
   essence   d. sophistry
7. divan—a. Oriental   b. disreputable house   c. fishing bird
   d. coffee room
8. divaricator—a. liar   b. muscle   c. transgressor   d. dallier
9. diverticulum—a. small marine creature   b. light entertainment   c. pouch   d. flaw in reasoning
10. divinity—a. transformation   b. white smock   c. sweet sur-
    prise   d. cream candy

The matchings are: 1c; 2a; 3b; 4c; 5b; 6d; 7d; 8b; 9c; 10d

1. filiation—a. winding a spindle   b. threading   c. joining
   d. fixing the paternity
2. insessorial—a. too closely related   b. unstopping   c. suited
   for perching   d. not scolding
3. foraminous—a. holy   b. holey   c. grainy   d. hungry

4. alectic—a. sharp b. unreading c. snappy d. carefully chosen
5. carnynx—a. color b. pedestrian c. trumpet d. gem
6. lituus—a. beach b. paper c. rite d. staff
7. salpinx—a. silencer b. horn c. detergent d. cathartic
8. aulic—a. hurried b. prophetic c. greasy d. courtly
9. aventurine—a. cautious b. reckless c. speckled glass d. foam rubber
10. avulsion—a. turning the eyes away b. hatred c. detached part d. scheming

Here are the matchings: 1d; 2c; 3b; 4b; 5c; 6d; 7b; 8d; 9c; 10c

It is easy to make up sets of words for PICK.

1. Select ten words, of a difficulty to suit the players.
2. For each, choose three words for "putative" meanings.

Two of these should have some semblance of relationship, but a false one; the third may have no connection whatsoever. Add, as the fourth, a valid synonym or definition. Thus for the word *provocative,* you might suggest: a. helping to prove b. tending to rouse c. noisy (*voc* is also in *vocal*) d. absurd

When making a series of such sets, vary the position of the correct word.

Any of the words given in MATCH may be used for PICK. Turn the pages of any dictionary for more.

KIP

KIP is a converse variety of PICK. The problem is to indicate what a word is not. Dictate a base word, and four choices—one of which is the antonym of the base word. Players are to pick the word opposite in meaning to the base word. Again, you can choose from the whole language, making your choices as tricky as you please. One way of adding complications is to make one of the alternatives a synonym of the base word. Here are just three sets, to point the path:

1. hebetude—a. carelessness b. accident c. irritability d. indifference

2. altruist—a. one who stands firm   b. noisemaker   c. show-off
       d. misanthrope
3. ostentatious—a. pretentious   b. retiring   c. insolent   d. sociable

Antonyms: 3b; 2d; 1c

OUST

This is another game of recognizing the right words. Make a set of four words. Three of these should be synonyms, or names of objects or ideas in the same group or class; the fourth word should be an outsider. Somehow, it does not fit with the other three.

Dictate or give copies of these sets of words to the players. Each must select, in each set, the word that does not belong. First to get all correct wins.

Here are a few to show you the pattern. Then make your own.

1.	rain	hail	frost	snow
2.	onion	cabbage	potato	turnip
3.	remainder	remnant	leavings	increment
4.	footballs	marbles	dice	tennisballs
5.	cone	circle	sphere	pyramid
6.	triangle	pentagon	ellipse	quadrilateral
7.	lobster	shrimp	oyster	crayfish
8.	chipmunk	woodcock	squirrel	raccoon

Oust the ones indicated here: 1. Frost does not fall.   2. Cabbage does not grow underground.   3. Increment is added, not left.   4. Dice are six-sided, not round.   5. All but the circle are solid objects.   6. An ellipse has no corners.   7. The oyster does not swim.   8. The woodcock is a bird.

SYNONYMBLES

A fine test of one's ability to use words lies in the distinction of synonyms.

Dictate five synonyms. Each player writes a sentence for each word, in such a way as to indicate the shades of difference in their meaning or use. Sometimes the denotation—the core of

meaning—of two words is hard to differentiate, but the conno-
tation—the aura of emotion or associated ideas—makes a clear
difference.

Players read aloud their sentences for the first word. The
group decides which is the most effective. Continue for the other
words.

Here are just a few samplings of synonyms; there are hosts in
Roget's Thesaurus:

brawny: muscular, sinewy, stalwart, robust, sturdy, strapping,
   strong
ill-will: malevolence, malice, hostility, malignity, rancor, ani-
   mosity
roomy: comfortable, spacious, capacious, ample, commodious
decree; enact, order, rule, prescribe, enjoin
faithless: perfidious, deceitful, treacherous, traitorous, untrust-
   worthy
cleave: adhere, cohere, stick, cling, hold
cleave: split, rive, rend, sever, sunder

You can add variety by giving each player a different set of
synonyms. Proceed the same way. Always, after each sentence,
discuss how closely the sentence has discriminated the precise
and proper use of the word.

WHENCE THE WORD?

The English language has almost double the number of words
of any other language. This is because it was formed by the
union of two great language groups, the Germanic Anglo-Saxon
and the Greek-Latin-Norman-French, and because it has always
borrowed freely from all other tongues. Wherever the English
went they found new words, if not new worlds, to conquer.

The two main coffers of our tongue are pictured in the conversation of Gurth the swineherd and Wamba the jester in Wal-
ter Scott's *Ivanhoe*.

Wamba complains that domestic animals, when they have to
be fed and tended, bear the serf Saxon names: sheep, calf, bull,

pig; but when they are dressed and served at table, they have become noble Norman mutton, veal, beef, and pork.

Since, after the Norman Conquest, while English was taking form, servants including nurses were Saxon, the majority of words learned in the first years of life were Germanic. These therefore seem the simpler, more emotional words. Norman words have overtones of thought, the aura of the study. Thus Saxon *thriving,* Latin *prosperous;* thus *nearness, proximity; needed* versus *necessary* and *essential.* When we speak of "the brotherhood of man" the French murmur *fraternité,* but English fraternity brings to mind a secret society at college. Motherhood is a blessing, maternity is a ward.

Writers naturally make use of such similarity and distinction. Shakespeare is especially fond of coupling a polysyllabic, abstract Latin word and a short, concrete Saxon one. Listen to Ophelia's exclamation over Hamlet:

> The *expectancy and rose* of the fair state,
> The *glass of fashion and the mould of form,*
> The observed of all observers, quite, quite down!
> And I, of ladies most *deject and wretched,*
> That sucked the honey of his music vows,
> Now see that *noble and most sovereign* reason,
> Like sweet bells jangled, *out of tune and harsh;*
> That unmatched *form and feature* of blown youth
> *Blasted* with *ecstasy.*

A clear example of the conjunction of the abstract and the concrete is in the remark of the rejected old servant Adam in *As You Like It,* picturing the lot of dependents when they are no longer of use:

> . . . unregarded age in corners thrown.

Adam continues:

> For in my youth I never did apply
> *Hot and rebellious* liquors in my blood,
> Nor did not with unbashful forehead woo

The means of *weakness and debility*.
    . . . Let me go with you,
I'll do the service of a younger man
In all your *business and necessities*.

How much of a word's background do you know?

SOURCY

Players are to write down as many words as they can. After each word, note the language from which it came into English. For each word correctly assigned, 1 point. For each different language, 2 points. You can use any large dictionary to check; there are thousands of words in my own *Dictionary of Word Origins*.

Here is just a slight indication of the variety of sources of our English words:

Saxon: do, make, go, see, here, to, mother, love; French: liberty, tempest; Celtic: gravel, skein; Italian: mountebank, pedant, spaghetti; Spanish: cork, cask; Portuguese: molasses, buffalo; Slavonic: mammoth, sable; Hungarian: coach, hussar; Basque: bizarre; Lapp: lemming; Arabic: algebra, admiral, lute, magazine; Aramaic: messiah; Hebrew: leviathan; Yiddish: schnorrer; Sanskrit: pepper, ginger; Hindustani: bungalow, pyjamas; Persian: scarlet, chess; Turkish: horde, vampire; Dravidian: mango, parish; Tamil: cheroot, anaconda; Malayalam: atoll, teak; Tibetan: lama, yak; Chinese: tea, silk; Japanese: soy, kimono; Malay: sago, bamboo; Malagasy: bantam, kapok; Tongan: taboo; Polynesian: tattoo; Hawaiian: poi, ukelele; Australian: kangaroo, boomerang; Egyptian: ebony, oasis; West African: gorilla; Sudanese: chimpanzee; Dahomey: voodoo; Bechuana: tsetse; Caribbean (via Spanish): hammock, hurricane; Haitian: potato, tobacco; Brazilian: tapioca, cashew; Peruvian: llama, puma; Mexican: chocolate, tomato; Powhatan: raccoon, moccasin; Algonkin: tomahawk, pecan; Penobscot: sagamore; Narragansett: moose, sachem; Ojibwa: wigwam, totem; Cree: woodchuck, pemmican; Canadian: toboggan; Natick: mugwump; Sioux: tepee; Eskimo: kayak, igloo

There are thousands more languages, and hundreds of thousands of words.

English has many doublets, words that have come from a single origin by diverse paths. Thus *regal* is directly from the Latin; from the same source but via Norman French comes *royal*. Saxon gives us a third word, *kingly*.

DOUBLET

Explain, with examples, what doublets are. Of ten such doublets, dictate just one word of each pair. First player to add the other words wins. (Note that in some cases words are triplets, or even quintuplets.)

Here is a short list of doublets. There are more in Appendix I of my *Dictionary of Word Origins*.

abbreviate—abridge; acute—cute—ague; adamant—diamond; appreciate—appraise; assemble—assimilate; astound—astonish —stun; blame—blaspheme; book—buck(wheat)—beech; cadence—chance; captain—chieftain; kennel—channel—canal; chattel—cattle—capital; disc—discus—dish—dais—desk; extraneous—strange; faculty—facility; flame—phlegm; flour— flower; genteel—gentle—jaunty; guarantee—warranty; guard— ward; hale—whole; musket—mosquito; ransom—redemption; two—deuce; monster—muster; naive—native; parable—parabola—parole—parley—palaver; praise—price; ratio—ration— reason; stack—stake—steak—stock; tulip—turban; zero— cipher

2

Raddles of Riddles and Such

The oldest riddles extant are in school books of ancient Babylon. Here's one from such a text, probably for persons studying to be priests:

> Who becomes fat without eating,
> Who becomes pregnant without conceiving?

Here is one from ancient Egypt, in an early English version:

> On yonder hill there is a red deer;
> The more you shoot, the more you may,
> You cannot drive that deer away.

Here is one from the Anglo-Saxons, who delighted in riddles:

> There is a troop of tiny folk traveling swift,
> Brought by the breeze over the brink of the hill,
> Buzzing black-coated bold little people,
> Noisy musicians; well known their song is.
> They scour the thickets, but sometimes invade
> The rooms of the town. Now tell me their name.

Other riddles have come down to us from all over the world. In the fourteenth century, the Arab Hajji Khalifa wrote a bibliography of riddlers, from which we learn that there were even specialists in the field. For instance, he lists two men who devised only legal riddles. For some reason, he does not list any that made illegal riddles.

Here are four from the Arabic:

It is a nag whose rider goes on foot. It bears its rider and its rider bears it. It is left at the door, all muddy. It never eats or drinks.

A friend whose companionship is not lessened as time goes on,
Who exerts himself diligently for my benefit,
In all the course of our being together I never met him,
And at the first good look I had of him he departed forever.

What is it that devours without mouth or stomach;
Trees and animals are food for it?
If you feed it, it becomes vigorous and thrives,
But if you give it a drink of water, it dies.

Take with you the one of full-moon face and pearly hue,
Of pure root and tormented body, who was pinched and stretched,
Imprisoned and released, made to drink and weaned,
Slapped hard, then pushed into the fire.

In the order of the riddles, the answers are: rain cloud; the rising sun; gnats; a shoe; a molar tooth, on its extraction; a fire; a loaf of bread, round, of course.

THE CONUNDRUM

Closely associated with the riddle is the conundrum, which also asks a question, but usually has a tricky answer. Sometimes the trick is that there is no trick.

Here are some conundrums. Try them, then try them on your friends.

1. What is it you can keep after you give it to someone else?
2. Why is it useless to give a chicken a pint of corn?
3. What trees are unchanged when they have been burnt?
4. What is it that has 22 legs and 2 wings, and may be seen in a field?

5. What crack is invisible?
6. If a tree were to break some windows, what would the windows exclaim!
7. Why is an author more free than a king?
8. What is it works when it plays and plays when it works?
9. What's the worst time of year to try to borrow a book?
10. Why is an auctioneer like a man with a fierce countenance?
11. Why do ducks go under water?
12. Why do they come up again?

1. your word　2. It always takes it by the peck　3. ashes　4. a football team　5. the crack of a whip　6. Tremendous! (tree, mend us)　7. He may choose his own subjects　8. a fountain 9. when it is Lent　10. He's always forbidding　11. for divers reasons　12. for sundry reasons

1. What word of five letters, take away two, leaves one?
2. What is it that ladies often look for but never want to find?
3. If I shoot at three birds on a tree and kill one, how many remain?
4. When is a window like a star?
5. To what should you answer nothing but Yes?
6. Why is a beehive (make this harder by saying *apiary* instead) like a spectator?
7. Why is carelessness like a ragged coat?
8. Why is there an ocean law against whispering?
9. What word becomes shorter when you add a syllable?
10. What do you break when you name it?
11. What's the difference between a mirror and a chatterbox?
12. What word makes you sick if you cut off a letter?

1. stone　2. a run in their stocking　3. none　4. when it's a sky-light　5. What does y-e-s spell?　6. because it's a beeholder 7. because it's a bad habit　8. because it's private hearing (privateering)　9. short　10. silence　11. The one reflects without speaking, the other speaks without reflecting　12. music

1. Why is churning like a caterpillar?
2. Why is a tournament like sleep?
3. Why is a proclamation like the 16th of a pound?
4. Why is necessity like an ignorant attorney?

5. Why is an interesting book like a toper's nose?
6. What's black and white, and red all over?
7. Why are women like facts?
8. Why is a bedcover like a narcotic?
9. Why is a woman's garret like a wild pitch?
10. Why are cats like butchers?
11. Why are chickens like farmers?
12. What's the difference between a watermelon and a grindstone?

1. It makes the butterfly   2. It's a knightly occupation   3. It announces (an ounce is)   4. It knows no law   5. It's red to the very end   6. a newspaper   7. They are stubborn things   8. It's a counterpane   9. It's erratic (her attic)   10. They mutilate (mew till late)   11. They like full crops   12. You don't know! I'd hate to ask you to slice a watermelon!

1. What do girls look for in church?
2. What is a good thing to part with?
3. What can be right but never wrong?
4. What is it that by losing an eye has only a nose left?

If a machine with three wheels is a tricycle, and one of two wheels is a bicycle, why isn't one with one wheel an icicle?— and one with five wheels a V-hicle?

1. the hymns   2. a comb   3. an angle   4. noise

Conundrums can be grouped about a particular topic. Here is a Conundrum Series to climb. What tree:

1. is prone to languish and sigh?	11. hemlock
2. is never seen on land?	10. cottonwood
3. is found only after a fire?	9. birch
4. is used around the neck?	8. elder
5. can be caught in the lake?	7. sandal
6. is found in every mouth?	6. gum
7. has been worn on pilgrimages?	5. bass
8. was born before?	4. fir
9. does a bad boy hate to see?	3. ash
10. gives goods to wear and stuff to burn?	2. bay
11. is part of a dress and part of a door?	1. pine

Have these with your meal! What is the food that:

1. is predicaments?	8. c.o.d.
2. makes the stream?	7. carp
3. is one of Noah's sons?	6. pike
4. is a woman's weapon?	5. salt
5. was the penalty for looking back?	4. tongue
6. is a country road?	3. ham
7. likes to find fault?	2. currant
8. bids you collect on delivery?	1. pickles

Time for orange blossoms. Try to name the bride of:

1. The chemist	8. Grace
2. The civil engineer	7. Carrie
3. The gambler	6. Peggy
4. The humorist	5. Mary
5. The clergyman	4. Sally
6. The shoemaker	3. Betty
7. The porter	2. Bridget
8. The dancing master	1. Ann Eliza

What cloth should the wife of the following wear?

1. woodcutter	20. cambric
2. dairyman	19. rayon
3. baseball player	18. homespun
4. fat man	17. lawn
5. baldheaded man	16. daycron
6. miner	15. tweed
7. equivocator	14. net
8. musician	13. cotton
9. refrigerator man	12. nylon
10. banker	11. serge
11. sailor	10. cashmere
12. Egyptian	9. frieze
13. furniture dealer	8. organdy
14. fisherman	7. orlon
15. gardener	6. drill
16. night worker	5. mohair
17. tennis player	4. broadcloth
18. gadabout	3. batiste
19. roentgenologist	2. cheesecloth
20. builder	1. corduroy

Fill up your glasses! What's a good drink for the:

1.	hypochondriac	10.	water
2.	shoemaker	9.	liquor
3.	undertaker	8.	ale
4.	drummer	7.	sauterne
5.	boxer	6.	mint julep
6.	financier	5.	punch
7.	carpenter	4.	seltzer
8.	invalid	3.	beer
9.	wife-beater	2.	cobbler
10.	promoter	1.	champagne

THE CHARADE

A charade is a riddle in which the word to be guessed is broken into syllables, each of which (and sometimes the whole word as well) is described in a more or less tricky fashion, or enacted.

The charade was borne into print in the year that our country was born. We have a recorded letter from a London lady, in 1776: "Pray send me some charades; but I shall not guess them as you do."

They must have been quite the vogue, for the very next year, in Sheridan's play "The School For Scandal," a character remarks: "I back him at a rebus or a charade against the best rhymer in the kingdom."

Charades then were usually rhymed; enacted charades came a century later.

Normally, the clue is a definition or a synonym. But you have to watch for tricky clues. Puns, anagrams (a word that can be rearranged to make the desired word), or even the literal giving of the correct word (which makes you hunt for another) may be tried.

Here is a sampling of assorted rhyming charades, which you can observe, and then try on your friends:

    1. My first is a thing for the feet,
My second is long at the head.
My whole is under the sheet
Before anyone is in bed.

2. My first is a crew or a troop or a band,
My second is wrought from the trunk of a tree.
My whole is, at signal, withdrawn from the land
Ere the steamship is steered to the sea.

3. My first in old taverns was sung or was read,
It was commonly rhyme without reason.
My second he is who gets out of his bed;
My whole is a thing for a season.

4. Through desert space, with fire and force
My first his way pursued;
His drink was water at its source,
My second was his food.
He had but little time for rest;
Across the burning sand
He bore my whole within his breast:
It was the King's command.

5. My first is a bank at the mouth of a harbor,
My second most persons are trying to get.
My whole the drygoods men with confidence offer:
"The best we have advertised yet!"

Here is a reversed and loose-ended charade:

6. A stranger comes from foreign shores,
Perchance to seek relief.
Curtail him, and you find his tale
Unworthy of belief.
Curtailed again, you recognize
An old Egyptian chief.

The answers, if you ponder them, will show you various patterns of clues.

1. mattress 2. gangplank 3. catchup 4. mandate 5. bargains
6. alien, a lie, Ali

Many charades are built up letter by letter. The pattern of these is much the same. On a rainy afternoon you can doubtless construct a score. For the time being, you can try this on your friends.

My first is in sorrow, but not in sad,
My second in girl, but not in lad,
My third is in near, but not in far,
My fourth is in train, but not in car.
My fifth is in sure, but not in slow,
My last is in reap, but not in sow.

(You can add to this "My whole is the season of hail and of snow," but that would be too easy. Instead, you can add: "My whole is the time when your fingers are fro—" When the angry players catch on, and ask why you omitted the last syllable, then it's time to say, with a superior smile—"Only the beatniks make a climax of Zen." It's best to make that answer very near the door. And it's just as well to omit any line describing the whole, which is Winter.

Here are some tricky charades. Dictate them, and give the number of letters in each word; I have put them after the clues. I fear, however, that the numbers will little avail you; what you need is the quick flash of fancy to discern the sly wordplay. Allow players three minutes, after they've got them down. If they're not through, the charades have got *them* down!

In all but the first of these, the clues are run together.

1. My first is nimble, my second innumerable, and my whole fatal   9
2. against the opening for nuns   7
3. how hungry the fool was to gain!   5
4. in the matter of the coffin-bearer, they practice   8
5. in a fold one can grow   8
6. tap the jar to get the style   7
7. worthy when you examine and eat   7
8. I'm in tipsy surroundings   5
9. greater supply on top, furthermore   8

This is what you have probably not found:

1. quicksand   2. convent   3. asset   4. rehearse   5. increase
6. pattern   7. condign   8. limit (*I'm* inside of *lit*)   9. moreover

The difficulty in fashioning such charades lies not in breaking words, but in devising clues that are at once precise and baffling. Such clues, after you have seen a few, must spring from your Pegasustained flight of fancy.

A few words you can work with are:

earthquake, rightly, pedantic, stealthy, mitten, elbow, steerage, spinster, misspend, movement, gorgeous, graceless, miscast, starboard, pedigree, sweepstakes, drawback, intone, gradation, mobilize, rumpus

The charade and the conundrum here walk on parallel tightropes, in a non-Euclidian universe.

Just to show that the English are not the only charadophiles, I give here a single one from the French storehouse:
Mon premier est le premier de son espèce; mon second n'a point de second, et j'espère ne te jamais dire mon tout.

Solution? adieu

More tricky fellows, these. The parts and the whole are tied together in clues that test the punster and the glib manipulator of words. Give the number of letters in each word when you dictate the clues—I've put the numbers after them, but that won't be of any great assistance, except to tell you that your flash was the true illumination, the proper Hippocrene.

1. banter not recommended for the elderly   8
2. wickedness in the right proportions gets together   10
3. reverse the covering for a traitor   8
4. wander, little devil, and grow better!   7
5. tavern praise makes a novelty   10
6. half a score strong in the pot   6
7. what the teacher didn't wear but gave   6
8. up the music on a poetic evening makes a triangle   7
9. the married woman is angry in the morning   5
10. outstanding orbs celebrate   9

The English work over this sort of thing for weeks. In case you haven't that much time, here are the words intended:

1. badinage 2. synthesize 3. turncoat 4. improve 5. innovation 6. potent (*ten* in *pot*) 7. lesson 8. scalene 9. madam (mad A.M.) 10. signalize

Names are easily broken or clued for Charades. Here's a disguised dozen.

My First:	*My Last:*
1. My whole makes small streams, yet it's afire!	
2. My whole is a tress that keeps a door shut.	
3. one animal	another's sound
4. good for a fire	high stretch of ground
5. pitch tents	ringer
6. what makes a speech	what makes the man
7. what the bell tolls	offspring
8. Spanish hero	joint
9. my whole will concede	
10. my whole makes hard blows	
11. happy	little rock
12. young fellow's name	his father's pride

I hope you have these figured out. Have players read their answers in turn. Each must give a sentence about the person he names. Here are the names:

1. Burns 2. Locke 3. Cowper 4. Coleridge 5. Campbell 6. Wordsworth 7. Nelson 8. Sidney 9. Grant 10. Knox 11. Gladstone 12. Edison

It may be possible for you to use the first or last names of some of your guests in this game, putting their names among the others.

ACTED CHARADES

This is a good pattern of enacted charades for a small group.

One player is chosen to start. He decides on a word or subject to work out, and writes it on a piece of paper. It may be a word he is going to act, one syllable at a time, or a proverb, or a title he will enact one word at a time. He gives the paper to the host, folded. (This prevents any change in the topic, in the middle of a performance.)

Without saying a word, the player than acts out his topic. First person to guess correctly has the next turn. Continue in this way; if the guesser has already had a turn, person on his right (nearest who has not yet had a turn) goes next. Play until everyone has had a chance; the one that guesses the most wins.

COUNTER-CHARADES

The first player writes down a word, choosing one that has several meanings, or has the same sound as another word. He enacts his chosen word. Persons who think they know the word raise their hands; one is selected. Without speaking, he enacts another meaning of the same word or sound. First player tells whether the second actor is right. If not, another player tries. Whoever acts the correct word has first chance with a new word, until everyone has had a chance. Player that guessed the most wins.

Counter-Charades may also be played by dividing the group into two teams. Second team must go on until it is right. Team that takes fewest tries wins.

For example; first may enact pain; second, pane; or bear (animal) may be followed by bear (to carry); ascent—assent; maze—maize; cymbal—symbol, or many hundreds more.

RHYMED CHARADES

A hundred years ago this game was very popular as an adult entertainment; it was called Dumb Crambo.

First person chooses a word to be guessed; he writes it on a piece of paper, which he hands to the host. He then announces a word *that rhymes with the word he has written.*

A volunteer is chosen. Without speaking, he enacts the word he thinks may be the one on the paper. He may enlist others to help act it out.

The first player must now say whether the word enacted is the right one. If it is not, another player enacts another word that rhymes. The one that acts the correct word then has a chance to start a new group of rhymes.

Continue until everyone has had a chance. If the correct guesser has already had a turn, the nearest person on his right who has not yet performed goes next. The player that has guessed most wins.

A game might move somewhat like this. The announced word, rhyming with the real word, is *fled*.

The guesser enacts:	*The giver answers:*
marriage	No, it's not wed.
eating	No, it's not fed.
marching or stamping	No, it's not tread.
fright	No, it's not dread.
kneading dough; baking	That's right! It's bread.

Simple rhymes that lend themselves to enacting are:

bat, fat, hat, mat, ghat, sat, cat, gnat, pat
loam, foam, home, roam, dome, comb, tome
armor, farmer, charmer, disarmer, harmer

Avoid sounds like *oo*—grew, gnu, shampoo etc.—as there are too many rhyme words. It's more fun to take tricky rhymes, where there are fewer words. Some such, that might be fun to act out, are:

follower, hollower, swallower, wallower
ceremonious, erroneous, felonious, euphonious, sanctimonious, parsimonious
keenly, meanly, queenly, cleanly, greenly

Any rhyming dictionary will give you more than you can use; but let your own fancy lead you.

Dumb Crambo, or RHYMED CHARADES, can also be played by dividing the group into two teams. Then the team that is given the rhyme word will keep on acting words until it hits the right one. The team that needs the fewer guesses wins.

THE GAME

This variety of Charades has recently been popular in Hollywood, and for some time was engineered on radio and television programs. Its addicts came to call it *The Game*.

This form of Charades is played by two teams. Each chooses a Captain. Each player writes a word, title, proverb, or the like, on a sheet of paper, folds it, and gives it to the captain. The teams then face one another.

One Captain passes one of the folded sheets to the opposing Captain. Without opening the paper, the Captain passes it to a member of his team.

The chosen member must act out the expression on the paper, and his own team tries to guess it. The time it takes to guess is noted.

Now the team that has guessed passes a paper to the other Captain, and the process is repeated. Each time, the Captain gives the paper to another member of his team. The Captain himself acts out the last one. The team that took the least total time wins.

While no words are spoken by the actor, his teammates, of course, guess as often as they can until they hit the right expression. The actor has come to be allowed certain stock gestures, more or less standardized. When he uses one of these, a teammate calls out what he means, to be sure it is understood.

Gestures of THE GAME

1. Hold up fingers to show how many words are in the expression. Then make a circle of middle finger and thumb if it is to be enacted as a whole. If not, one finger for the first word, two fingers for the second, and so on. If a word is to be broken into syllables, right hand chops on back of left hand, as many times as separate syllables are to be acted.

2. Yes or No (right or wrong) is shown by the usual nod or shake of the head.

3. To show that something doesn't count—or, if the team is not guessing from the actor's pantomime, to show that he's going to act the same thing over—actor crosses hands back and forth in front of his face, quickly, palms facing out.

4. If the guess is close, "warm," actor motions with both hands in toward himself: Get closer! Come on!

5. If word or idea should be smaller (mountain to mount or hill) bring palms of hands slowly toward one another, as though squeezing. If larger, or plural (bush to bushes, or tree), move them slowly apart.

6. Pushing right hand away, to the side, means actor is leaving out a small word, which can be guessed from the rest of the expression: if, an, the, and, of, or the like.

7. Other natural gestures suggest themselves:
     hand extended to shake: friend, friendship, shake, etc.
     hands joined in prayer: religion, bible, piety, etc.
     pointing: to light, to an object, to part of oneself.
     pointing at floor means *here*.
     pointing at man or woman indicates sex.

Good hunting! The team should make sure it understands a gesture, remember, by speaking what it means.

In addition to words elsewhere in the book, here are a few it has been fun to act out:

ingratiate, nocturne, aspect, moonshine, parapet, concord, strawberries, handout, buccaneer, pilgrimage, sausage, anticlimax, infancy, honesty, corollary, matrimony, mercenary, infirm, handcuff, hateful, piteous, tawny, testify, gallop, haughty, shadow, tenderly, papacy, flatulent, pinafore, tango, straighten, granulate, dogmatize, gladsome, target, illustration, gallantry, tendrils, ingenuity

The rest may be left to your ingenuity.

THE PUN

The pun is one of the earliest and most widespread forms of word play. Puns go back at least as far as Eve, the letters of whose Hebrew name (h v h) spell talk.

Why puns should be so pretendedly unpopular is a puzzle. Even the Snark always looked grave at a pun.

Shakespeare in two sonnets plays upon his name, Will. Rabelais, when sick, asked to be clad in his robe (*domino*), for *Beati qui in Domino moriunt:* Blessed are they that die in the Lord. Thomas Hood on his death-bed remarked: "Now the undertaker will earn a livelihood" (urn a lively Hood).

Perhaps the most famous pun in literature—not counting the pun with which Jesus authorized the Catholic Church—is the answer of Odysseus when the Cyclops asked his name. In English, what he said is *Noman;* but in Greek it is *Odys.* This is a symbol of the task of the artist: he must give all of himself. For if the artist tries to hold back any of himself it is inevitably the Zeus—the god in him—that drops away, and no man indeed that remains!

Another artistic principle, "Take care of the sense, and the sounds will take care of themselves," is the Duchess's perversion (in *Alice in Wonderland,* that pillbox of parody and pun) of the old English saying, "Take care of the pence and the pounds will take care of themselves."

When I was in Turkey, I met some Kurds, and admired the way they weigh their whey.

The trouble with nudism is that it is all hide and no seek. An apple one day led to clothing.

Puns are dragged in so often that they grow bedraggled.

Tell a historian: The pious men of Plymouth, when they reached the Rock, fell first upon their knees and then upon the aborigines.

Go to the poet. Thomas Hood records, when the luckless lover dies at the end of his poem "Faithless Sally Brown":

> They went and told the sexton and
> The sexton tolled the bell.

G.W. Carryl, picturing a stumbling drinker, and turning a trope to a toper, declared:

> If a swallow cannot make a summer
> It may bring on a summary fall.

A wealthy maid, wooed by an inveterate smoker, said she'd marry him if he gave up smoking:

> "To have your Anna, give up your Havana."
> But he, when thus she brought him to the scratch,
> Lit his cigar, and threw away the match.

Pay heed also to P. T. Barnum, who built his fame on the maxim: "The public likes to be fooled." When his circus began, what is now the Side Show was then the Main Attraction. He exhibited such things as the Swedish Nightingale, Tom Thumb, Jumbo, and other curiosities. On the principle that the female of the species brings bigger fee than the male, Barnum featured the cow elephant, the doe, the dam, the hind, the leopardess, the tigress. And when the crowds became very large, he put up a big sign: "This way to the egress!"

PUNNY

This is a game for sophisticates. Dictate five subjects for punning. Allow ten minutes for the players to write their efforts. Then each reads his sentence for the first subject; the group decides which is best. Continue for all five subjects. I repeat the remark of the man who boasted he could pun instantly on any subject. "The King!" At once he replied: "The King is not a subject."

Some subjects that have given scope to pundits are:

range; petty; horse races; the radish; uncle; bunk; crime; woe; trouble; blunder

Blunder naturally brings to mind *bus*. To buss, of course, is to kiss. The Romans had three words for kiss, distinguishing the pious kiss of respect, the matter-of-fact kiss of kinship, and the ardent kiss of love. We have dropped the hearty buss from our tongue, we rarely use the overlong osculation, so that we are left with only the all-duty kiss.

BUST

Remind the players that buss means to kiss. Then ask them to identify these kisses (words with the sound *buss* in them).

1. kiss the wrong party	12. omnibus
2. kiss your uncle	11. filibuster
3. Hurry, she's waiting for it!	10. robust
4. before a kiss	9. busted
5. He made it!	8. syllabus
6. Listen! We're at it!	7. incubus
7. write it down	6. arquebus
8. foolish kiss	5. buster
9. Here's Theodore!	4. Erebus
10. on the lake afterwards	3. combustible
11. the young girl kissed her	2. buskin
12. kiss all the girls at the party	1. blunderbus

THE BONER

Closely allied to the pun, save that it pretends to be accidental, is the boner.

In a play on Broadway a youngster, asked if he knew the word semantics, replied: "I know anti-Semantics." I am anti some antics, myself. (Seldom my own.)

What the Americans call a boner, the English label a howler. They think you will howl at the likes of these:

George Washington is the man who said he never told a lie.
What is the shape of the earth? Obsolete.
Name a hibernating animal. An Irishman.

When there is a genuine boner, it may dog you. Having dug your hole, you proceed to fall into it. Samuel Johnson trod this path, speaking of an author who married his printer's devil. "She did not disgrace him; the woman had a bottom of good sense."

Among the listeners, Hannah More hid her face; several others tittered. Johnson glared, then reiterated: "I say that the woman was fundamentally sensible."

The twelve-year-old author of *A Young Girl's Diary,* sponsored by Sigmund Freud, wonders why so many good words are hush-hush. That really depends upon the circumstance. The laundryman spoke with exemplary exactitude when he said to the nun in charge of the wash: "Good morning, Sister. Have you any dirty habits?"

THE BULL

The bull is a boner tied to a paradox.

When we say that someone is throwing the bull, the figure is drawn not from the Spanish toreador's arena, but from the American cowboy's corral. Often at the rodeo you can watch the contest to see who can throw the bull fastest; I have seen a young bull grounded in nine seconds flat. This does not get to the core of the figure, unless the cowboy is wearing dungarees.

But the verbal bull, sired not on the Spaniards or the Americans but on the Irish, is a horse of another color. It is also of a lengthy lineage. Here are a few early members of the family:

The only way a gentleman will look at the faults of a lady is with his eyes shut.

A noble woman, lamenting her childlessness, remarked that in some great families this was a hereditary misfortune.

Sir Richard Steele invited a bore: "Sir, if you come within ten miles of my house, I hope you will stop there for the night."

Milton in "Paradise Lost" declares:

> Thus incorporeal spirits to smallest forms
> Reduced their shapes immense.

A servant girl, writing home to her family, said that the women she lived with were so rich that even their flannel petticoats were silk. This reminds me of a charwoman we once had, who wished she were so rich she could scrub the floors in a silk dress.

In pedigreed bulls one may not at once discern the fatal flaw; one just looks to see how far is the nearest shelter. So with Milton above; but how can *incorporeal* spirits reduce the shapes that they have not?

Thus too with the description of a duel: One party received a slight wound in the chest; the other fired in the air, and so the matter ended.

There is never an end to bull.

THE SPOONER

The Spooner, or Spoonerism, is a common slip of the self-conscious. The tongue tangles over what is to come, and the first sound of a later word gets ahead of itself, changing places with its natural predecessor. The rather nervous Reverend William Archibald Spooner (1844–1930), Warden of New College, Oxford, once dismissed a student: "You have deliberately tasted two worms; you can leave Oxford by the town drain!" He fortified a timid groom with the assurance: "It is kistomary to cuss the bride."

A quick mind can still spin a good Spooner. Try some of your own sentences, or some that you hear or read. You will be surprised what oddities can come from exchanging the front sounds of the main words.

PERVERB

Both boners and Spooners can be shaped from familiar proverbs.

Dictate five proverbs. There are some listed at the end of this book. Allow five minutes for the players to "pervert" them, by Spooner or boner or pun or bull. Each player in turn reads his first Perverb; the group decides which is most amusing. Continue for the other four.

WELLERISMS

Explain that the Wellerism is named after Sam Weller, in Dickens' *The Pickwick Papers*. Sam was fond of illustrating his ideas with quaint images. Here are a few:

Hope our acquaintance may be a long 'un, as the gen'l'm'n said to the fi' pun' note.

Away with melancholy, as the little boy said when his school-missus died.

The wery best intentions, as the gen'l'm'n said when he ran away from his wife 'cos she seemed unhappy with him.

Now we look compact and comfortable, as the father said when he cut off his little boy's head to cure him o' squintin'.

Give players paper and pencil. Each player is to write five general ideas, or remarks, ending with a comma followed by the word *as*.

Exchange papers. Each player is to add a Wellerism to each of the sentences on the paper he now has. Group decides which are the most amusing.

Some possible beginnings are:

There's many a slip, as . . .

Patience pays, as . . .

There's always another side, as . . .

There's always room at the top, as the operator said when the elevator plunged down, out of control.

There's safety in numbers, as the worker said when he applied for social security.

Life is a scramble, as the driver said when his truckload of eggs overturned.

Two less familiar aspects of word play may here be noted. PREPARTEE. This occurs when someone has thought of a clever remark, a repartee or other witticism, and he carefully directs the conversation so as to give him the opportunity to display his cleverness. He may even enlist his wife's aid, telling her about it before they reach the party. This process is successful only when unrecognized.

The converse of Prepartee is what the French call *l'esprit d'escalier,* staircase wit. This is the clever remark, rebuttal, or verbal comeuppance one thinks of when it's too late, on the way home. Of course, there remains the hope that, next time, one may be able to slip the wit in, through Prepartee.

3

Building Blocks of the Language

Words build upon letters. It's just a question of finding the right combinations. We call a literary figure not a man of words but a man of letters. If it comes to that, we seem to prefer a man of few words.

We must also be careful about letters. A man may speak all he will to his beloved, and the sounds will evaporate with the dew; but let him court her in letters, and who knows when his letters may come to court!

From the first two Greek letters we draw the name of our alphabet. There are several games that can be played, just with our 26 letters.

ALPHABET

Here is a game for learners. How well do you know the alphabet?

First player says "Z." Next player at once says "Y." So on, each player in turn, quickly through the alphabet backwards. Better have a timer, with the alphabet in front of him. Anyone giving the wrong letter, or hesitating more than 5 seconds, drops out.

If done, start again, backwards, omitting the 5 vowels.

If done, start again, backwards. Tell players who are left to omit every *second* letter.

If there are survivors, start again, backwards. Tell them to omit all the consonants. (Catch in this: Y and W can be counted as vowels.)

If there still are survivors, start again, backwards. Tell them to omit all letters whose capitals are printed with a horizontal line. No hesitating more than five seconds! This ought to get them down! (Such letters are Z,T,L,I,H,F,E,A.)

Any players now left may be assumed to know their alphabet.

You can play this Alphabet Game with teams instead of individuals. Divide the group into two teams. They should stand facing one another. The teams alternate, each person in turn giving the appropriate letter. Any one dropping out sits down. The team that holds out longer, or with the more survivors, wins.

ALPHABETWIXT

Here is a slightly more complicated game.

Each player writes ten consecutive letters, for example, l m n o p q r s t u. Pass the papers to the right. Each player must now write a sentence of ten words, each word to begin with a letter, in alphabetical order, on the list he now has.

The group decides which sentence is cleverest.

A ONE ALPHABET

If your friends know the 26 letters of the American Alphabet, you can spend a pleasant period by having them demonstrate their knowledge.

Each is to create an Alphabet Arrangement, as in the baby books, but using odd, unfamiliar, or punning words and phrases, rhyming if they can. Have each one read his product in turn; the group decides which is cleverest.

Comic alphabets have been built since Jonathan Swift; Eric Partridge has made a goodly gathering of them. Yours might start, for example:

A is for apatite, often blue-green;
B for bizarre, where no goods can be seen;
C is for candied, which hardly is frank;
D for dessert, but don't run from your rank.
E is for earwig, keep it out of your hair;
F —
    but I leave you to take it from there.

ALPHABETTER

Here is a trickier game the letters of the alphabet abet. It's fun to play, and very easy to make.

Here's how to make an Alphabetter.

1. Take any word, preferably of nine or more letters, all different. For instance, corpulent.
2. Write this word in capitals, widely spaced. Over it write all the letters of the alphabet not used in the word.
3. Scramble these other letters, and tuck them before, after, and between the letters of the chosen word. You now have an alphabetter.

Here's how to play Alphabetter.
You now have the 26 letters of the Alphabet in one long mixed list. Dictate this to the players. Tell them to find the word, with its letters all in proper order, that is hidden in the Alphabetter. Tell them how many letters there are in the word. For instance, the Alphabetter may look like this:

S H C B W O X M R Y Q P K U Z I V J L G E F D N A T

The word, you remember, is corpulent.

The game may look easy when you know the word to find. Here are a few to try yourself, before you try them on your friends.

J F Q A D C Z E P X T G I H O N U M S K L V W B Y R
N L H V Y Q U P S T O F K D Z B E G R A M J I X C W
B L C O Y N W J G R A I K X T F Q U H Z D V S E P M
Q R H A P D V I M O X L J Z U W C Y F E G B N K T S
V S T A J Q W I F K N U G Z B L C P O D E R H M X Y
T A H Q U Y G P L O Z V D N E X R J M W I F C B S K

The words in these Alphabetters—not in the right order, are longitude, vainglory, facetiously, hypodermic, radiolucent.

You can, of course, for any word, tuck in the other letters in many different orders, each of which creates a new problem. In fact, you will notice that in the set above, there are six Alphabetters and five words. One of these words has been used twice.

I've done this just to show the possibilities; you can work with any word at all in which no letter is repeated. A fairly long word, or a word with an odd combination of letters, helps the alphabet abet you best. Here are a few such words:

bracketing, constipated, plenitude, valedictory, porcelain, mythopeic, zymogenic, stenographic, zygomatic, slotmachine, universal, quicksand, subordinately, nefarious, profluent, sympathizer, profanity, workmanship, rudimental, playgrounds, signature, formulated, forensical, tenaciously, girandole, documentary, comedians, xylophage, measuringly, formidable, solemnity, questionably, handsomely

CATEGORIES

This is an alphabetical game of sorts. You decide in advance which sorts. There are many sorts or categories to choose from, according to the ability and the interests of the players. There are birds, beasts, flowers, sciences, poets, kings (but not cabbages), authors, movie stars, baseball players, cities, rivers, gems, book titles, characters in fiction, vegetables, foods, foibles, qualities.

The players agree on four categories, and write each one at the top of a column. Then the host, or players in turn, give a letter—perhaps four letters in all. These are written one under the other at the left.

Problem: to write the name of an item in each category, beginning with the letter on that row. Thus there may be selected:

QUALITIES	VEGETABLES	CITIES	BIRDS
C caution	cauliflower	Cleveland	chickadee
L love	leek	London	linnet

First one to complete the list wins.

Variation

Instead of giving separate letters, give a four-letter word (boat, beak, cone, drip, etc.) to be written down the side. Continue as before. Continue until each player has given a four-letter word. After each two words, you may if you wish change the categories.

Variation

Take only one category. Write that category along the left side, one letter under the other. These letters must now become the first letters of names of items in the category. Each player now writes as many items as he can think of beginning with each letter. The one with the most—but at least one for each letter—in five minutes wins.

ALPHABET COURTSHIP

The first player repeats aloud the sentences given below, and supplies words, all to start with A. Second player does the same, but all his words start with B. Continue around the players and the alphabet. Any player stumped drops out; survivor wins.

Sentences: I love my love with an A because he is (first player may say) affectionate. I hate him because he is—ambitious. I feed him with apricots and applesauce. His name is Alexis and he lives in Albany. He took me to the Alleghany Arms, and treated me to almonds and ale. We were married in August, and now I am seeking alimony.

Next Player: I love my love with a B because she is beautiful. I hate her because she is boastful. She fed me with bread and butter. Her name is Bella and she lives in Belfast. I took her to the Belle Sauvage and treated her to beer and bananas. We married at the Bureau, and now I am tamed by my better half.

Here's how Alice did it, through the Looking-Glass: I love my love with an H, Alice couldn't help beginning, because he is happy. I hate him with an H because he is hideous. I fed him with—with ham sandwiches and hay. His name is Haigha, and he lives—"He lives on the hill," the King remarked simply, without the least idea that he was joining in the game.

Verses that run through the alphabet are numerous. The most famous of these is the Siege of Belgrade, in which every word of the line begins with the appropriate letter:

> An Austrian army awfully arrayed
> Boldly by battery besieged Belgrade.

The rest is in the companion book to this one, *Playing With Words*.

ALPHABUILD

Without verse, you can build up your own alphabet stories. The first player gives a sentence that mentions a specific item in a category. It may be "I hope to go to Albany" or "For dinner today, I had some appetizers." The item he gives must start with the letter *a*. The next player must continue, repeating the words, and adding something in the same category that begins with *b*. "For dinner today, I had some appetizers and some buns." Better have someone write down the items, as a check.

By making his addition odd or long, a player will add to the troubles of those that follow. Any player that omits any words or gets any wrong, drops out. When Z is reached, all the survivors, if any, must repeat the entire alphabet of items. If more than one still survives, they keep on the accumulation and start through the alphabet a second time.

The accumulated series might sound something like this:

I hope to go to Alexandroupolis, and then to Berchtesgaden, and then to the Cabinet Mountains, and then to Deer Flat Reservoir, and then to El Alamein, and then to the Forbidden City, and then to Goodenough Bay, and then to Halicarnassus, and then to Idaho City and then to Jericho, and then to the Komi Autonomous Soviet Socialist Republic, and then to Lithuania, and then to the Monongahela, and then to No Man's Land, and then to Orange Free State, and then to Palma de Mallorca, and then to Queensland, and then to Randall's Island, and then to Saskatchewan, and then to Turkestan, and then to Union City, and then to Venezuela, and then to Westphalia, and then to Xenia, and then to Yokohama, and then to Zalamea, Zanesville, or Zwyndrecht.

If you can get that far, you will have no trouble whatsoever with an alphabet of accumulated foods, or animals, or whatnots.

Variation

If the single words of this game prove too simple, double them. The words must be related, as an adjective followed by a noun. The first word of each pair must start with the appropriate letter. Continue this until all but one have dropped out for forgetting or confusing the words.

Such an accumulative series might begin:

Anxious mother, bouncing baby, cautious canary, Doctor Caligari, empty bottles, fine fettle, glorious Fourth . . .

Variation

Have *both* words in each pair begin with the same letter. This might go along:

Aloof aristocrat, bawling brat, costly candelabra, diagnostic doctors, effete effeminates, fizzling firecrackers, guzzling gorillas, happy Hooligan . . .

Variation

This is to be played as a writing game. Each player goes through the whole alphabet. Each writes a two-word phrase beginning with A, then one beginning with B, and so on. Lists are read aloud. You might—if you are giving prizes—give one for the person finished first, and one for the list that the group deems most amusing.

ALPHATRIP

First player names a place he'd like to visit. Next player must repeat this place, and add another place—*the first letter of which is the last letter of the place just named.* And so on: each must repeat all the previous places, and add one.

Anyone that cannot go ahead in 20 seconds drops out. If players are dropping out too slowly, cut the time allowance.

Also, anyone that fails to repeat all the places already named, correctly and in order, drops out.

A series of places might run:

I'd like to go to Alaska, Alabama, Alcatraz, Zurich, heaven, New Haven, Newport, Trinidad, Denver, Reno, Oswego, Otranto, Oconto, Oderzo, Oglio, Ohio, Okovanggo, Olimpo, Ontario, Ondo, Oporto, Orono, Oslo, Outjo, Oviedo, Owego, Oyo, Okefinokee. Whew! I thought we'd never get through owing things!

Variation

If the memory works readily, and the game flags, try adding something you take to the place. It must be appropriate. For instance:

I am going to Alaska and shall take my sister; then to the Rocky Mountains with my riding boots; then to Snow Valley with skis; then to the Sahara with sunglasses; and so on until memory or words fail.

ASSOCIATION

This should move along quickly. A leader starts it; then he does not play but keeps the record.

Leader says a word. At once the next player says another word suggested by the first. Next player says a word suggested by the second word. And so on around the group, each quickly giving a word suggested by the one before. The leader jots down each word as spoken; it will help if he knows shorthand.

After about 15 words, the leader says without warning: "Reverse!" At once the next player (in the same order around the room) repeats the last word. Next player repeats the word before the last, and so on until the first word is reached again.

If any player gives the wrong word, or in 5 seconds cannot remember the word, the Leader gives the right word, 1 point is scored against the player, and the game goes on.

Repeat the process for a second round; then again. After four rounds, the player with fewest points against him wins.

A series of words might run like this:

Glove, ball, pitcher, well, water, goldfish, China, red, white, blue, unhappy, smile, teeth, dentist, pain, neck—Reverse!

SPELLING

Reformers are usually dedicated persons, wrapped in their role. They are often fanatics, unable to recognize any point of view in the matter save their own. This is good for their project, for they go into it body and soul.

The rest of us should not be swept off our feet. Look, for instance, at spelling reform. How simple to spell enough *enuf!* The reformers have cold reason on their side. Two sorts of person may object:

1. Those like my nephew, who says he has no intention of learning to spell any way, because when he grows up he'll dictate to a secretary.
2. Those that enjoy words, who know that the spelling of a word is a capsule history.

Let us be careful. Let us Bee. . .

The Bee—because it kept everyone as busy—was a popular way of getting folks together in our Colonial times. Especially enjoyable was the husking Bee, when the corn was stripped of its husk and hung to dry. One of the pleasant rules of this Bee was that you could kiss the girl with a red ear.

And every school had its Spelling Bee. They still had them when I was a pupil in elementary school. In the school-wide competition—with no trace of compunction, nor any after display of the regret that stirred in the schoolgirl of Whittier's poem —a girl I knew shamelessly put me into second place.

Although there may be minor differences in the organization, the spelling match is played in one basic way.

SPELLING BEE

Divide the players into two teams, on opposite sides of the room. The Referee has a list of words. He pronounces a word from the list, then gives a definition, then pronounces it again. First player spells the word.

First player on the other team, if he thinks the spelling is right, so indicates. If not, he gives the spelling he thinks correct. The player that is wrong drops out. If a word is wrong, and the next player does not challenge promptly, any player on the opposing team may challenge. If no one challenges, and the word is still wrong—after at least one player on each team has dropped out —the Referee spells the word.

The game continues in this fashion until only the champion— the Queen Bee—is left standing.

(Why is it that women are usually better spellers than men? A prominent psychoanalyst has told me he believes that women are, in general, smarter than men. He believes that the story of Eve's being created out of a rib of Adam is just a ribbing, or rather a symbolic attempt by early man to dethrone women from their leadership in the primitive matriarchal society. Today, women no longer covet the strappings of power; they are content to rule. Of course, this book is only a book about words! Let the women cast their spell.)

Here are some teasers to spell. Try them on your friends, or in a spelling match:

forfeit, fierce, vein, grief, gazetteer, mischief, neither, rein, abridge, brief, parallax, palliative, cadaverous, impecunious, vituperative, foreclosure, fricasseed, toboggan, xylophone, portable, tequila, accessibility, believe, seize, beguile, foment, extraneous, indigenous, omniscient, luxuriant, gnash, predilection, contrariety, irascible, dinghy, mausoleum, weight, foreign, eschscholtzia, height, niece, harass, embarrassment, labyrinth, predacious, paroxysm, gaudy, estuary, optometry, maraschino, bouillon, nausea, geisha, annular, relieve, peccant, receive, flocculent, emollient, blatant, sapient, synthesis, repetition, protein, ecstasy, diocese, eatable, sovereign, sacrilegious, abbreviate, fissile, gusset, adversity, fiery, paraphernalia, beleaguer, chartreuse, eczema, untenable, bureaucratic, tintinnabulation, hyssop, legerdemain, therapeutics, turbulence, ceiling, sleigh, archetype, flaccid, optimistic, hydrangeas, gullible, jurisprudence, voracious, gondolier, apparel, insatiable, juxtaposition, bizarre, confectionery, avoirdupois, ricochet, hauteur, myrmidon, inscrutable, diphtheria, parallelopiped, vinaigrette, pusillanimous, laughable, dhow, pyx, whippoorwill, arteriosclerosis, schottische, seizable, tetanus, tortoise, mutable, choreography, laryngitis, quadrille, bivouac, concomitant, bibliophile, demurrer, amethyst, chamois, heterogeneous, phycology, phthisicky, ctenoid

Be sure to give the meaning, or a clue, so that, for instance, a voracious person will not be confounded with one that tells the truth. When in doubt as to pronunciation, consult a dictionary.

Spelling, as we know it today, is just the current stage of a continuing process. The word *cushion* has had in its past, mainly in old wills and inventories, almost 400 forms. Among these are cuyschun, quishin, whysshene, quyszhynge, cowssing.

The name Shakespeare has been written in 13 ways; the name Mainwaring, in 130!

Shaw has laughed at our ways of representing sound by saying *ghoti* spells fish; but try *ghoughphtheightteeau*. This, more or less obviously, spells potato: *p* as in hiccough, *o* as in dough, *t* as in phthisic, *a* as in eight, *t* as in etiquette, *o* as in beau.

Let a letter alone, and look at a number. Numbers and letters have been associated in many ways, from earliest times. The Hebrew letters are also numbers—aleph, bet, gimmel, one, two, three . . . We still use letters for Roman numerals: I for 1, V for 5, X for 10, L for 50, C for 100, D for 500, M for 1000.

In many languages the letters have been given numerical values. The pseudoscience of numerology has been built upon this relationship. This may have something to do with the choice of a "lucky" new name by a motion picture starlet, but it usually has little connection with the current "numbers racket."

The peoples of the Near East found significance in relations between numbers in their names and dates in their lives. The Western world has not spent much time at this game, although the number of the Antichrist has been figured out as a number now innocently displayed atop a new Fifth Avenue skyscraper—666. This number has therefore been found—by their enemies

—hidden in the names of such persons as Julian the Apostate, Luther, Mahomet, and Napoleon.

Occasionally a chronogram has been found in a sentence, to fit a fact. Thus the first letters of the sentence "My Day Closed Is In Immortality" give us the year 1603, the year in which the first Queen Elizabeth of England died.

THE NUMBERS GAME

Take words that are built of letters used for the Roman numerals. Among such are: Cid, id, lid, Vic, vim, mix, dim, mid, mild, civil, livid, civic.

Make clues for such words. For instance:

1.	More power to you!	5.	lid
2.	A Spanish hero	4.	dim
3.	Well behaved	3.	civil
4.	Not so bright	2.	Cid
5.	Take it off!	1.	vim

Or you can give the clues in a sort of charade, with mathematical hints. Here are two for you:

My last is half my first.
My second and fifty make one more than my third.
My whole is easygoing.

Five times my second gives my last.
Twice that's my third, but it doesn't count.
The rest may pass, but my whole will surpass.

These, as you have figured out, are mild and excel.

REBUS

The Rebus (a Latin word meaning *with things*) commonly uses pictures to stand for words, but sometimes it works with letters. A very very thin capital A, for instance, is obviously in no sense **A** broad—namely, Mark Twain's book, Innocents Abroad.

The REBUS can continue as long as ingenuity and patience

permit. More than half the letters of the alphabet, standing alone, sound like words—A, C (sea, see), G, I, L, M, N, O, P, Q, R, T, U, Y.

Other letters can be put and pronounced together to form words. Among these are EZ, KN, XPDNC, CD, NV, XL, TP, LEG, XTC. You can make games of them.

LETTER WORD

Give an example of letter words (SA, essay). Allow players five minutes to write down as many as they can think of. Score 10 points for every word no one else has. Other words score 10 minus the number that have them. Highest score wins.

Variation

Make up clues (synonyms or definitions) for some letter-words. Give the clue, which should mention the number of letters. Players are to write down the correct letter word. For example:

1. What three letters name a foe?	6. IC
2. What three letters are a thing that is?	5. XLNC
3. What two letters are too much?	4. DK
4. What two letters fall to ruin?	3. XS
5. What four letters greet an ambassador?	2. NTT
6. What two letters are below freezing?	1. NME

NUMBER, PLEASE!

Ask the players to write, down the left margin of the sheet you give them, the numbers from 1 to 10

Next to each number, they are to write as many words as they can, beginning with the spelling or sound of the number. Allow five minutes; the one with the most words—provided there is at least one word for each number—wins.

For instance:

1. won, wonderful, wonder-worker, onesided
2. tool, toothache, toothsome, tooth, toodle-ooh!, twosome

3. threefold, threne
4. foursome, fortune, forge, fortify
5. fiver, fives
6. sixty, sixes, six-footer
7. seventy, sevens, seven-league boots
8. ate, ataxia, eighty
9. ninepins, ninefold, Ninus' tomb (in *A Midsummer Night's Dream*)
10. Tenor, tenure, tenner, tennis, tentacles, tenderfoot

With a few of the numbers, the list runs rather thin, but there are enough to fill the time and test the players.

NUMBLES

Leader asks a question. Allow two minutes for every player to write an answer, which has in it a number or the sound of a number. Explain that either an actual number or the sound (*for*tune, segre*gate*) must be in the answer. After all the questions, answers are read aloud; the group decides which are the most amusing or apt. You can make up any questions, silly or profound. Here are a few, with answers:

1. Why did you come here to-night?
2. Who can best inspire a poet?
3. Why is there so little cake left?
4. What was the answer of Wordsworth's little maid?
5. How old are you?
6. If X is the unknown quantity, what's left when it's evenly divided?
7. When can I hope for a kiss?
8. What digit rhymes with devices?
9. Who was victor in the contest?

16. Ingratiate
15. To get your fortune told
14. Tenderfoot
13. Vituperation
12. I wonder
11. I forget
10. Nein
9. The one that won
8. Six (devices are tricks)

10. How did the German answer the beggar?

11. What was the answer to my first question?

12. What's on the other side of the moon?

13. What's the $64 word for swearing?

14. What would you be to a cowboy?

15. Why cross a gypsy's palm with silver?

16. What happened when the woman in a gray suit went to dinner?

7. That remains to be seen.

6. Five (V)

5. That's naught to you.

4. We are seven.

3. Because you ate the rest

2. One of the nine muses

1. Just for fun

NUMB

Mathematics, of course, uses a language of its own, in combination with words most persons know. The pure language of mathematics, numbers, leaves many persons numb.

Mathematical puzzles may lie wholly within the special field, or be intertwined with logic, or speared upon a word. Let us look at a simple sample of each.

1. For pure mathematics. A man walks at the rate of 4 miles an hour on level ground, 3 miles an hour uphill, 6 miles an hour downhill. He sets out at 2 P.M. on irregular terrain, and walks steadily until he returns to his starting place at 5 P.M. How far did he walk?

2. For logic. An express train leaving Chicago travels at an average speed of 60 miles an hour toward New York. A freight train from New York travels at an average speed of 30 miles an hour toward Chicago. Which train is nearer New York when they meet?

3. For language. A man had 24 pigs and 4 pigpens. He put the pigs in the pens in such a way that, if a girl walked around them, she would always come to a pen with a number of pigs

nearer to 10 than the pen before. How were the pigs arranged in the pens?

1.   On level ground, the man would walk 1 mile out and 1 mile back in ½ hour. Uphill and down again, he would take, for a mile each way, ⅓ hour plus ⅙ hour, which is ½ hour. Thus, on the entire trip, he would average 2 miles per ½ hour, or 4 miles an hour. Since he walked for 3 hours, he traversed 12 miles.

2. This is a teaser. Since we don't want the trains to meet head-on, we'll put them on adjacent tracks. You might think that, when they meet, they are at the same distance from either city. But trains "meet" when their engines touch a line drawn perpendicularly across the two tracks. At this moment, by its often considerable length, the freight train is nearer New York.

3. The farmer arranges his pigs in the pens in this order: 8, 10, 0, 6. The girl walks around: ten is nearer to ten than eight; nothing is nearer to ten than ten; six is nearer to ten than nothing; eight is nearer to ten than six. It would work just as well for a boy.

WORD SIZE

A word may be ponderous without necessarily being weighty. We may, contrariwise, pack a world into a five-letter word.

Shaw complained that *love* is too small a word for so big a burden.

O is a big fish in the waters of Hawaii. Homomonukunukuaguk is a little one.

Lyoyd George was born in Llanfairpwllgwyngyllgogerychwyrndrobwllantysiliogogogoch, in Wales. When you reveal this, don't heed the company's wails, but tell them there is no whaling in the lake in Massachusetts named Chargoggagoggmanchaugagoggchaubunagungamaug. This should have them all agog.

Most impressive in English are the ten "thunderwords" in James Joyce's *Finnegans Wake,* each of 100 letters. The seventh,

I am told, symbolizes the fall of the Irish hod-carrier Tim Finnegan from his ladder, of Humpty Dumpty from the wall, of man from the garden, and of Lucifer from bliss. Here it is: bothallchoractorschumminaroundgansumuminarumdrumstrumtruminahumptadumpwaultopoofoolooderamaunsturnup.

Sometimes, however, the larger, the smaller. The noun singular *hair* may imply a headful; plural *hairs* implies that they, if not their days, are numbered. Once there were three proud tailors on Bond Street. One put up a sign: Best Tailor in the Empire. The second saw this, pondered, and put up a sign: Best Tailor in England. The third read the two claims, took thought, and put up a modest sign: Best Tailor on this Street.

SIZING

Each player writes a sentence of not less than ten words, using the smallest number of letters that he can. Sentences with fewer than 50 letters are read aloud; the group decides which is cleverest.

Then each player writes a sentence of not more than ten words, using as many letters as he can. (In this sentence, *a, and, the, is, are* may be used and not counted.) Sentences with over 70 letters are read aloud; again the group decides which is cleverest.

When a foreigner learns English in his late teens, it is often noted that he tends to employ lengthy, learned, polyloquent, inkhorn phrases. But the learners most assiduously (and often acidulously) verbose are the parrots, for they always talk in pollysyllables.

GHOSTS

The most famous of word games played without any equipment is GHOSTS.

First player gives a letter. Second player gives another letter, which, in order after the first letter and with other letters added, can make a word. Next player, repeating the letters already given, adds another. So on until a word of four or more letters is spelled. Object is, *not to be the one that completes a word.* Player that ends a word (of four or more letters) is "dead."

Once a word is ended, next player gives a letter to start a new word. The process is repeated.

When a player is "dead" three times, he is a "ghost." He then takes no part in the playing, but "haunts" the players. Whoever speaks to a ghost becomes one, and also drops from the game.

If a player cannot think of a word to form, with the combination of letters that has come to him, he may challenge the player before him. If this player can give no appropriate word, *he* is "dead"; if he can, the challenger is "dead."

Obviously, in choosing a letter, you must try to build toward a word that will not come around and end with yourself. And you will try to change endings—if the letters come back to you, instead of b.a.k.*e,* which makes you "dead," you can say *i* for b.a.k.i.n.g.

You can also play that four-letter words do not count.

Ghosts haunting, and players becoming a ghost if they talk to one, are parts of the game often dropped. Instead of making a player "dead," you may score a point against him for each word he ends or each challenge he loses. At the end, the one with the *lowest* score wins.

DOUBLE-GHOSTS. This is a trickier form of Ghosts. All the rules of Ghosts apply. The difference is that, after the first letter has been given, each player in turn must specify whether his new letter is to be put before or after the letters already given. The new letter may be put at either end.

For instance, let us suppose the letters given are t.i.t.l. At this point, the next player avoided the word *title* by saying *i.* The next said *n.* Now it's your turn. You say *"N* before the *T—* n.t.i.t.l.i.n"; the player two after you is likely to be caught with the word *entitling.*

There is more fun, however, if you slyly slip letters in front earlier in the game, not just waiting to get out of a scrape. For example, if someone begins with k: Say "k.k." Then "o.k.k.," and you are on the way to *bookkeeping* or the like.

All sorts of tricky combinations can develop in this two-end variation of Ghosts, challenging the ingenuity and verbal skill of the players.

PUNCTUATION

The two major functions of punctuation are to aid toward clarity and to mark the rhythm.

Errors in punctuation can be costly. American economic history still speaks of the $12,000,000 comma, a misplaced mark in the tariff law that cost the United States that sum in uncollectable duty before the slip was corrected.

When Bishop Orleton advised Gourney and Maltravers, in 1327—"Refrain not to kill King Edward is right," did he want the pause to come before or after the negative? The two men thus counseled murdered the king.

Sometimes errors in punctuation are intentional, for humor. We find an example of this in the play *Roister Doister,* written by Nicholas Udall while he was headmaster of Eton, 1534–1541. Ralph Roister Doister has a copy of a letter a scribe has prepared for him, to Dame Custance, "mine own dear coney, birde, swete-heart, and pigsny." This is the way clown Merigreeke reads it to her:

> Sweete mistresse, whereas I love you nothing at all,
> Regarding your substance and richesse chiefe of all,
> For your personage, beautie, demeanour and wit
> I commend me unto you never a whitte.
> Sorry to heare report of your good welfare . . .

and so on for thirty-six lines of insult. From the righteous wrath of Custance—who anyway is a virtuous married woman—Ralph tears back in a rage to the scrivener, who looks up in round-eyed innocence, and reads:

> Sweete mistresse, whereas I love you—nothing at all
> Regarding your substance and richesse; chief of all

> For your personage, beautie, demeanour, and wit.
> I commende me unto you. Never a whitte
> Sorry to heare report of your good welfare . . .

and the dumbfounded Ralph looks upon the innocent clown.

Another type of readjustment may be called for in works that seem to say one thing but that, astutely read, say quite another. In the following verses, for example—printed in Harper's Magazine of August 1855—the knowing male read line 1 then line 3 then line 2 then line 4 of each stanza. I give but the first and the last stanzas:

> That man must lead a happy life
> Who is directed by a wife.
> Who's free from matrimonial chains
> Is bound to suffer for his pains.
>
> Confusion take the men, I say
> Who no regard to women pay.
> Who make the women their delight
> Keep always reason in their sight.

The distinctions effected in written thought by punctuation are usually supplied, in speech, by pauses or inflections. To omit the comma or the pause in the following remark would be to provide a different observation: Women are pretty, generally speaking.

The statement: "Charles the First walked and talked half an hour after his head was cut off" would be less astounding if a semicolon and a comma were judiciously inserted.

PUNCT

Give an example of an expression the meaning of which changes with the punctuation. Thus:

> PRIVATE! No Visitors Allowed.
> Private?　　No! Visitors allowed.

Players in three minutes think of and write such double-barrelled expressions. Read them aloud; the group decides which are cleverest.

AMAZED AMERICAN

Idioms, idiotisms, and idiasms abound on every tongue. Translate the German greeting: "How does it go with you?" The French: "How do you carry yourself?" The Englishman no less oddly questions: "How do you do?" One can imagine a foreigner wondering: "How do I do what?"

Picture a Frenchman that knows a little English talking to a pretty girl that knows no French. Being Parisian, he starts at the end point: "Je t'adore!"

She looks around wonderingly, and protests: "But the door *is* shut!"

To cover his embarrassment, he laughs. Seeing nothing to laugh at, she exclaims: "You're funny as a crutch!" Now it is his turn to be bewildered. Has he understood her? Is there a joke, or is someone really lame?

Recently a series of jokes—now printed on cocktail napkins —was built around the notion of misunderstanding and manhandling Paris chatter. It was called Fractured French. In this pattern, "une affaire manquée" (a deal that fell through) becomes "monkey business." "Cul de sac" (blind alley) is heard as "Fix an ice bag!"

These form a variation of a game I used to play, many years ago. Its point was to mystify those around by pronouncing a good English sentence as though one were speaking a foreign tongue. Our stock example was "Pas de lieur roan ka neux," which any Redskin might recognize as "Paddle your own canoe."

Later, while teaching English to foreigners, I came upon an East European example that has been hailed as classic. A first-year student read a sentence: "Ee summa timmess plwa bahl." On the black board was spelled: "I sometimes play ball."

AMAZED AMERICAN can be more fun. The idea is to take an English idiom or figure of speech—and take it literally.

One way to do this is to prepare drawings in advance. Hold

them up; players write down the meaning they guess. The one that has the most correct wins.

For instance, draw a picture of a boy hanging from a clothesline. Have a clue ready, in case the drawing does not get across. In this case, you might say: "And he wasn't wet, either!" The expression is: They left him high and dry.

Here are some phrases that can be used for Amazed American:

It's in the bag; fifth column; bite the dust; paint the town red; get into a scrape; grass widow; haul over the coals; an eye-opener; Bronx cheer; knee high to a grasshopper; sow his wild oats; up to scratch; a wet blanket; eat out of house and home; go to the dogs; give the cue.

Variation

Instead of looking at drawings, explain, with an example, what Amazed Americans are. Each player in turn acts out the literal meaning of such an expression; the others have to guess what it is. The actor tells when they are right. When all have had a chance to act, the one that has guessed most wins. Here are a few more expressions:

raise the roof; ride a hobby; go begging; have an axe to grind; eat crow; bark up the wrong tree; a ghost writer; miss the point; make the flesh creep; fly in the ointment; bear him out; his heart is in his mouth; carry the day; have me on the carpet; blind alley; cut him dead; limb of the law; pass the buck; keep tabs on; cap the climax; by fits and starts; fly off the handle; bury the hatchet; pave the way; on its last legs; get the point; a dark horse; take the floor; small talk; it won't hold water; plume oneself; make him the goat; throw cold water on.

NIMBLEBREAK

There are many words that can be soundly twisted into other terms. Break them gently, and they form new parts. Start with the clue. For instance: "It's easy to see he's a white man." Go back to "This a plain Aryan" and you can reach disciplinarian.

Explain as above. Dictate ten clues; after each, allow 45 seconds for the players to exercise their ingenuity, traveling backwards on your path to the original word. The one with the most correct wins.

Here are some Nimblebreaks:

1. I swore at them roundly.	20. sunrise
2. Did you shout?	19. necromancy
3. the way a guy speaks	18. lonesome
4. If not, listen!	17. Rosicrucian
5. You can't see, but she's wearing it!	16. Rorschach test
	15. romancing
6. The building's getting good care.	14. expose
7. a stupid fellow	13. damnation
8. I've eaten already.	12. blazon
9. and we intend to eat it, too!	11. beautiful
10. on the floor of the car	10. automat
11. Don't give her a bite more!	9. archaic (Our cake)
12. It's afire!	
13. the enemy, of course	8. admiration
14. a former attitude	7. adobe
15. Italian gives a song	6. superfine
16. Try out the green hut	5. pantheon
17. Keep away from the sunburned sailors!	4. jeer (Did you hear?)
	3. addiction
18. I'm broke.	2. jell
19. in a petty mood	1. accustom
20. Get up, my boy!	

Variation

Instead of dictating clues, dictate ten words. Players are to figure out a Nimblebreak for each word. The group decides which are most amusing. Here are a few words, with sentences:

1. arrears. My mom always wants me and me brudder to wash in back of arrears.
2. denial. Crocodiles and Cleopatra lived along denial.
3. falsify. I can balance a ball on my head, but it falsify move.

4. insulate. My Mom always asks my Pop why he gets insulate.
5. Rotterdam. I wish our neighbor would Rotterdam head off.
6. diploma. Last night we had trouble with the toilet and had to call diploma.
7. mournful. After Thanksgiving dinner, I'm always more'n full.
8. extradition. Eat all you want. There's an extradition the kitchen.
9. notwithstanding. The bookkeeper wore out the seat of his pants, notwithstanding.

Variation

Explain a Nimblebreak. Each player is to think of five such words, and write sentences for them. The group decides which are most amusing.

4

Sound and Nimble Journeyings

There have been many discussions as to which are the most beautiful words in the language. Some psychologists and aestheticians, however, maintain that we do not really dissociate a word from its meaning, and that it is the meaning that dictates the attitude. Thus Max Beerbohm observes: "There is no word which, by itself, sounds ill or well . . . A sentence can be musical or unmusical. In detachment words are in their sound no more preferable to one another than are single notes of music . . . You are pleased with the sound of such words as gondola, vestments, chancel, ermine, manor-house . . . You murmur them luxuriously, dreamily. Prepare for a slight shock. Scrofula, investments, cancer, vermine, warehouse. Horrible sounds, are they not? But say gondola-scrofula, vestments-investments, and oo on; and then lay your hand on your heart and declare that the words in the first list are in mere sound nicer than the words in the second. Of course they are not. If gondola were a disease and if scrofula were a beautiful city, the effect of each word would be exactly the reverse of what it is."

I'd as soon trust the words of a sibilant sibyl! Is a word like a single note of music? Is it not, rather, like a chord? A carefully selected chord will have more beauty of sound, I should venture

to say in the majority of strikes, than a random thrust of fingers
at piano keys. Combined sounds, then, regardless of the se-
duction of meaning, may seem beautiful or ugly. Or at least
appropriate or inept. Naturally, tastes will vary; one man's bleat
may be another man's conversion. The sound of ichthyosaurus
(protract that soar!) may appeal to a romantic soul, on a moon-
lit evening in a canoe; gibberish (give it the *j* start!) may pulse
a gay rhythm to someone skipping along the dunes.

Although in good writing the sound should fortify the sense,
there are some words in which the sound and the significance do
not establish a harmony. Thus the long ē and the final hiss of
the word *peace* seem to me out of place for so gentle a dream;
the most concordant uses of the word are those of:

1. Patrick Henry in his vehemence echoing Jeremiah, crying,
"Peace! Peace! when there is no peace" and of:

2. Rumor, when Shakespeare in his percipience has her say:

> "I speak of peace while covert enmity
> Under the smile of safety wounds the world."

Think, then, of the ugliest, or the most amusing word sounds.
Words like syzygy, or slantindicular, or bellicose, or ipses, or
craniodidymus (two-headed monster!) or ironmongery, or ira-
cundious (which let's hope you're not!), or ursicide, or werther-
ian (which is not kissing kin to pickwickian), or wordfactur-
ologist (which you may think at this moment I am, but these
are all good dictionary terms!), or zumbooruk, or zymosimeter,
or zwinglianism, or xanthocyanopia (in which I have a son
expert), or wyliecoat (where Robert Burns expected lice to
abound), or yachtswoman, or yohimbine (not so bad, this one;
lovers in darkest Africa seek it out), or yttriferous, or musimon,
which is a form of musmon, which is the same as mouflon, which
is an alternative form of moufflon, which is a wild Sardinian
sheep. Then there is amygdalotomy (which is also tonsillec-
tomy), as well as anacleteria, which you can read about in
The King Must Die, but which bears no relation to anaclastics,
nor to the dziggetai of Mongolia or the dzeron of the Middle
Kingdom.

SOUND OFF

Players make a list of what they think the ten ugliest (or you can say funniest) sounding words in the English language. Emphasize that it is not the meaning but the sound they should have in mind. There will be lots of warm argument before the group decides which list is best.

Did you ever shiver when you heard a word, just at the sound? Has a word ever made you tingle with delight? Sometimes, even when you do not know the meaning, the sound may give you a premonitory stir.

If you consider combinations of words, you open all the wonders of poetry. Notice how, of the simplest ingredients, the poet brews his magic.

A—the most common article
thing—the vaguest word in the language
of—anyone's possession, a slovenly sound
beauty—the vaguest word in the field, used for any taste, outworn and indefinable
is—the common copulative, like the knot in a string of sausages
a—here it is again!
joy—Rapture! the romanticist's exclamation, and ephemeral dream
forever—the lie sentimental

Keats put these unpromising materials in a row, and made one of our most moving poems:

> A thing of beauty is a joy forever,
> Its loveliness increases . . .

SOUND FEELINGS

Sounds snared in single snatches are less malleable, but they often convey the suggestion of a feeling. For example, SL may portend the underhand, sinister, sliding, slipshod.

Call this to the attention of your group. Allow them three minutes to write down all the words they can think of, with this sound and such a suggestion. Two points off for every word the group decides does not have that feeling. Then the one with the most words (one point each) wins. Here are some to weigh:

slide, slattern, slipslop, sliver, slush, slow, sly, sling, slack, slippery, slither, slam, slobber, sloven, sloop, slouch, slubber, slice, slim, slip, sloppy, slump, slab, slander, sluice, slothful, slit, slogan, slough, sleuth, slick, slime, slipper, slink, saliva, slake, slalom, slang, slash, sleek, sleep, slaver, sludge, slum, slant, slaughter, sled, sleeve, slender, slug, slumber, slap, slave, sledge, sleigh, sluggard, slur, slubberdegullion

You can raise a similar question with other combinations.

Words with SW may suggest a sudden turn or spin, dizziness: swoop, swirl, swerve, sideswipe, swindle, and many many more.

SP may suggest a point, a spit of land, a spar, or particularly (SPR) a moving from a point (spring) perhaps without leaving it (spread, span): spectacle, spiral, splice, sprinkle, etc.

STR may suggest a motion or extent, an exertion, strain, stretch: stratagem, strict, stride, structure, strumpet, etc.

Not every start is sound, if you get my meaning. Ask a friend if he's familiar with Scotch names. Have him pronounce M-a-c-i-n-t-o-s-h- Then M-a-c-d-o-n-a-l-d- Then M-a-c-i-n-t-y-r-e- Then M-a-c-h-i-n-e-r-y- Ours is sometimes referred to as the Machine Age, but that doesn't scotch our troubles.

> If you don't know what you're after
> You will surely feel man's laughter.
> If you don't do as you oughta
> You're a target for manslaughter.

DOUBLETONES

Give an example of a word (spelling) that has two sounds, each with a different meaning. Several such are given below. Players should think of five such doubletones. For each, every player should write two sentences, one sentence using the word in one meaning, the second sentence using it in another meaning

—BUT, *instead of writing the word, the player leaves a blank where the word should be.* Exchange papers. Each player now fills in the blanks on his new sheet. The one that fills them all properly first, wins.

Here are some spellings that change their sound with their sense:

bow, lead, recreation, genial, minute, reformation, concha, wound, does (the verb; the animals), rise (the noun may be pronounced rice), pier (also one that pies type), none (long o, a church service), refuse (three sounds), bouse (meaning to drink is pronounced booze), housewife (the sewing-kit case is pronounced huzzif).

SHIFTONES

There are many words in the language which are accented on a different syllable when they are used to perform different functions in the sentence. This process of shifting the stress, which has already become a *fait accompli*—That's a practice many writers indulge in, using a foreign phrase when they have an exact English equivalent! The shifting of stress, I was saying, which has become an accomplished fact with many words, is still in the process with many others. If you watch, you can hear our language changing.

Over television, on New Year's Day, 1961, I heard several shifts of this sort. The announcer of the Rose Bowl game spoke of a "fast de'fence." Other speakers said dis'charged and re'search.

And the broadcaster of the commercial for "Exquisite Form" said "exquis'it," which some dictionaries now allow as a second choice, but which sounds to me like an illiterate's apology: "Exquisite, please!" Accenting the first syllable gives an opening exclamation followed by delicate tones, which fit the meaning ex'quisitely.

Equally disturbing it was, to hear an elegantly dressed lady at a Broadway premiere, twice repeating that New York is really a most *hospitable* city, and all three times stressing the spit!

In certain compounds, the accent shifts, as we say refer' but ref'erable; prefer', pref'erable; despise', des'picable; though here too common usage is reworking some words. Thus the British Broadcasting authorities ruled that formidable should be accented on the first syllable, except in H. M. S. Formidable, which takes the stress amidships, as a good ship should.

Point out, with an example, that some words change accent according to their use in a sentence. Allow players five minutes to write sentences in pairs; each pair properly uses one word in two differently accented ways. The word must be exactly the same in both sentences; only the sound shifts. The player with most correct pairs of sentences wins.

This accent shift is not a sign of current bad habit, but an allowed feature of the language. Probably many of the shiftings now frowned upon will, in another decade, be standard speech. A poor speaker may just be ahead of his time! Here are some shifts now standard:

subject, object, reject, convert, convict, contact, content, progress, present, conduct, confine, converse, combine, concord, protest, expert, transfer, adept, console, costume, construct, insult, recess, incense, augment, prolate, compound, consort, digest, invalid, permit

Other words of one spelling but two sounds include:

entrance; sewer; resent; multiply (Things may be multiply interrelated); tearing (cloth or eyes); number (This hand I've been holding out of the car window is number than the other.). A stingy fellow nettles you more than a stingy nettle. One who prays is a prayer; what he prays is a prayer. A little boy interested in butterflies and moths found in the library a book that considerably confused him: *What Every Young Mother Should Know.*

R and L, though they look different, may blend on the palate. They are frequently interchanged. While a Chinese may see a "Melican man," a Japanese may wish him a "Happy Horriday."

Watch the interchanging in the stars: Greek aster—disaster, astronomy; Latin stella—constellation; French étoile (Old French esteile)—Estelle, Stella; German Stern—star. See it in pet names: Mary—Molly; Katherine—Kathleen; Sarah—Sally; Harry—Hal. Our officer the *Colonel* is pronounced like the inside of a nut.

S is a bastard sound. Pindar excludes it from his odes. In Castillian Spanish *c* before *e* and *i* is pronounced not *s* but *th*. The French drop it from many Latin words, for instance: tête, from Latin testa, pot; bête, beast; fête, feast; crête, crest, tempête, tempest.

The repetition of sounds is the delight of children. An infant may go on and on just lilting "La la la la." The habit does not die with our growing.

Nursery rhymes are rich in reduplication, especially in their nonsense refrains: hey diddle diddle; tweedle tweedle twino; Tweedledum and Tweedledee; twiddle-um, twaddle-um, twentyone, eerie oarie ourie, you are out. They also give us reduplicated names, like Georgie Porgie and Rowley Powley.

DOUBLETONES

Simple game: Each player writes as many reduplications as he can in three minutes.

Variation

For a little more complexity, play it with sentences. Give players two sheets of paper. On the first, they write as many doubletones as they can in three minutes.

On the second sheet, each player writes six sentences. Each sentence uses a reduplicative word, BUT *instead of writing the word, they leave a blank*. The second sheets are exchanged; players now have three minutes to fill in the blanks on their new sheet.

Score: First sheet: For words no one else has, 10 points. Other words, 10 points minus the number that have the word. For words the group thinks especially effective or unexpected,

2 points. Second sheet: For each properly finished sentence, 3 points. (There may be an appropriate word that was not in the mind of the one that wrote the sentence; the group must decide if the word is apt.) For any inappropriate word or unfinished sentence, 2 points off. Highest score wins.

Here are some sample sentences for such a game:

1. Don't make so much—! I can hardly hear myself think.
2. The kind of—you keep company with, I'm beginning to suspect you're just an overgrown delinquent.
3. He walked along the bog, that sunny morning, with his lips puckered to a whistle and a—in his heart.
4. "I have had ample sufficiency," said the sated diner; "any more would be—."
5. The bachelor Charles Lamb in one of his essays revealed his regret at never hearing the morning—of tiny feet.

On the first sheet, balanced for these sentences, were the words: 5. pitter-patter; 4. flippety-flop; 3. tooraloora; 2. riffraff; 1. clitter clatter

And here is a registration of some doubletones:

shipshape, ticktack, gawky pawky, rosy posy, fol-lal, hobnob, tick tock, wishywashy, hippity hoppity, razzle dazzle, pingpong, tittle tattle, mewling puling, bawling squalling, see-saw, hurly-burly, slish slosh, itsy bitsy, blackjack, mumbo jumbo, tickle-tackle, folderol, niminy-piminy, huggermugger, snipsnapsnorum, bricabrac, honky-tonk, splish splash.

There are three major patterns of reduplication:

1. Exact repetition: cancan, bonbon, murmur
2. Change of vowel: chitchat, crisscross, zigzag
3. Change of consonant: hodgepodge, hickory dickory, hokey pokey, heebie jeebies

FLIPANSEE

Many English words ending in -ip can be balanced with words ending in -ap. Thus: rip-rap, slip-slap, strip-strap, snip-snap, tip-tap, scrip-scrap, sip-sap, clip-clap, hip-hap, lip-lap, nip-nap.

Half-tied are grip-grapple; dip-dapple, but dipper-dapper. And would you allow eclipse-collapse or claps?

At any rate, here's a Game of FLIPANSEE.

Make two teams. First player has an -ip word in mind. He uses it in a sentence, BUT instead of speaking the -ip word he says *cow*. First player on the opposing team must guess the word, and at once give a sentence using the corresponding -ap word. If it does not fit, the first player challenges him; the one that is wrong drops out. Then the next player gives a sentence; continue until one side is all out.

The play might go like this:

Player   1. I had a cow of gin last night.
          2. You poor sap! I hope you got home sober.
          3. Somebody tried to cow me yesterday, but I turned the tables on him.
          4. Was it that Jap you were talking about?
Player   3. I challenge you; I was thinking of clip.
Player   4. I took the word to be gyp. It fits what you said.
Referee (Host): Third player is Out.

And on you go. Instead of cow, you may use some other word, like bellyful, or frankincense.

TEASING

There was an early English form of teasing listeners on, as though with hymnal exhortation:

O take a pill! O take a pill! O take a pilgrim home!
O for a man! O for a man! O for a manifesto!
Como take a pee! Come take a pee! Come take a peep at baby!

Teasing repetition has seen a minor revival in 1961. With a punning twist, one of the songs in the musical *Kean* speaks of the "so so so-so social whirl."

HOMONIMPS

It is the existence of words of the same sound that permits the homonimps retort courteous. For instance:

You may think you're great, but I have a nutmeg grater!
You may think you're witty, but I know a poet Whittier!

If you can think up another of these, you ought to be a good player of UNDER THE SHEET.

One person leaves the room. The others agree upon a word of varied meanings, or a homonym. The person sent out comes back. He asks each person in turn a question. The person must answer in a sentence that uses some meaning of the chosen word —BUT instead of saying the word, he says "Under the sheet."

After asking as few questions as he can, the questioner guesses the word. Keep note of how many questions he has asked. A wrong guess counts as a question.

Then another player goes out, another word is chosen, and the process is repeated. Continue until every player has had a chance to guess. The one that asks the fewest questions wins.

The game might go something like this. Suppose the word chosen is vain-vein-vane.

Q. What were you doing yesterday afternoon?
1. It's under the sheet to ask me.
Q. How far away were you?
2. Near enough to see the weather under the sheet.
Q. What state were you in?
3. Iowa, and the prize pig that won the blue ribbon was quite under the sheet

And so on, until the word is guessed.

Here are some homonyms you can use:

pennants-penance, knead-need-kneed, ere-e'er-air-heir, foul-fowl, role-roll, mantel-mantle, canopies-can o' peas, ruff-rough, parasite-parricide, coward-cowered-cowherd, arc-ark, beach-beech, sinus-sign us, bass-base, current-currant, cousin-cozen, faun-fawn, firs-furs-furze, vale-veil-vail, cession-session, de-mean-demesne, counsel-council-consul-console, break-brake, muscle-mussel, road-rowed-rode, comfort-comfit, ceiling-sealing, wheel-weal-we'll, mall-maul, pedal-peddle, dissent-descent-de-cent, die-dye, symbol-cymbal, impassable-impassible, missal-missile, coin-coign-quoin, there-their-they're, board-bored, load-lode, seam-seem-see'em, fare-fair, bowl-bole-boll, aisle-isle-I'll, male-mail, beau-bow-bo, blue-blew, plain-plane, saporific-soporific, gilt-guilt, suede-swayed, sane-seine, pair-pare-pear-père, interned-inturned, rabbit-rabbet, pause-paws-pores-pours, sweet-suite

Variation

Give the players five sounds, each of which can be used for more than one meaning. They are to write a separate sentence for each use they can think of, for each sound you have given.

Score: For the most sentences (different meanings) 10 points. For any use no one else has, 10 points. For others, 10 minus the number that have that use. For sentences the group thinks exceptionally ingenious, 2 points extra. For any misuse, 5 points off. Highest score wins.

Variation

Give the players two sheets of paper. On the first, they list all the homonyms that come to their mind, in three minutes. On the second, they then write sentences using four pairs of homonyms, BUT instead of putting down the homonyms, they leave blanks (eight blanks). Exchange second sheets. Each player must now fill in the blanks. Completed sentences are read aloud.

Score: For every set no one else has, 10 points. For others, 10 minus the number that have the set. For homonyms of more than two forms for the one sound, 5 points for each beyond the two. In the sentences, for each filled in, 3 points. For each one wrong or left blank, 2 off. Highest score wins.

Here are a few more of our tongue's homonyms:

site-cite-sight, spare, pan, read-reed-rede, seen-scene, tier-tear, tare-tear, flue-flew, cannon-canon, martial-marshall, gall-Gaul, quarts-quartz, loan-lone, busted-bustard, seer-sear-sere, team-teem, claimant-clamant, pervade-purveyed, hoard-horde-whored, waist-waste, whether-weather, chased-chaste, rapt-rapped-wrapped, bolder-boulder, very-vary, sarcophagous-sarcophagus, write-wright-right-rite, meed-mead-Mede

Homonyms afflicted the Romans too. Thus malo malo malo malo is translated:

> I'd rather be in an apple tree
> Than an evil man in adversity.

NIMBLES

Hopalong Hopeful—that's anyone that wants to play—can jump from word to word in bantering mood. Follow as you would leap from solid clump to clump in a peat bog, by the exercise of Nimbles. Try not to get all wet.

Here's a Nimble I sent on a postcard to a friend, after we had discussed weather forecasting:

Why is a meteorologist like a Stone-Age savage? A meteorologist is a weather man. Whether is a conjunction. A conjunction is a joiner. A joiner is a club-man. Need I say more?

Nimbles go back beyond my memory. I retain a partial hold upon a Nimble that rejoiced my childhood. The middle part flits:

. . . a breeze is a zephyr; a zephyr is a yarn; a yarn is a tale; a tail is an appendage . . .

Perhaps some old word-fellow can send me the beginning and the end.

Try making a few Nimbles with me. Let's start with bore. A bore is a drill. Drill is exercise. Exercise is strengthening. A strengthening is a support. A support is a hold-up; a hold-up's an attack. A tack is a fastener. A fastener is a sticker; a sticker's a label; a label's a sign. A sine is a term. A term is a period. A period is a full stop. And we've brought the bore to a full stop . . .

When I reached the period, I knew what my opening would be: Can you make a bore stop talking? Sure!

Let's try again, with the girl friend: Hello, Mary! Merry is jolly. To jolly is to kid. A kid is a youngster. A young stir is a new dancer. A nude answer is the naked truth. To tell you the truth, this is going awry. I'll have a rye with ham . . . When you get into this sort of thing, it's best to start over.

Remember, you make up the question to fit the starting and stopping words, after you've come to a good stop.

Here's a Nimble to put the pretentious in their place! What's a show-off? A show-off is too posy. How do you know that?
A show off is a turkey (theatrical flop). A turkey is a fowl. What's foul mars. Mars is a planet. A planet is a satellite. A man who sat till light is a watchman. A watch, man, is a timer. To tie myrrh is to garland. To garland is to posy. A show-off is too posy. Q. E. D. and over the mountain!

Simple words for nubile Nimbles can be some that begin with A. By turning this letter into the separate article, you have a new word, as *alone* may be turned into *a loan*. Here are some more of such words:

adrift, awry, aware, assist, accrues (cruse, cruise), attest, ahead, aversion, anneal (an eel), aboard, attempt, amass (mass: lump or ceremony), about, abut, abridge, acclaim, abase

Or you can reverse the process; reaching a base, you can then note that abase means to lower.

Here are some words with more than one meaning, which can be leapt across for Nimbles:

desert, bunting, blank, yarn, skirt, cow, chase, fleet, rear, boss, birch, box, row, file, saw, till, gull, bark, relish, court, shed, star, net, swallow, husband, set, trap, redress, stool, chest, toll, post, sole, vamp, fuse, buck, bowl, woof, graze, ash, joint, tart, race, gore, down, cotton, palm, brief, tie, stage, variety, rue, asp, peach, drove, crow, scour, bat, cycle

And here are two more Nimbles just composed—that is, I preserved my composure—to show how they can move along.

What should a man with a paunch do? Paunch is a belly. A belly's a bag; a bag's a purse. To purse (lips) is to thrust forth; to thrust forth is to project. A project is an intention; an intention's a design; a design's a purpose (We could have skipped the design!). A purpose is a thought; a thought's opinion. A pinion is a wing; a wing's an appendage. An appendage is a tail. A tale is a story. A storey is a floor. To floor is to knock down; to knock down is to reduce. And that's what a man with a paunch should do.

What shall we do with a man who wants a bribe? A bribe is a consent rate. (I really started this with concentrate, then broke it up and moved a step backward.) Concentrate is to think; to think is to reckon; to reckon is to figure. A figure is a shape. To shape is to fashion. Fashion is style; a stile is a gate; a gait is a pace; a pace is a walk. Tell him to take a walk!

Let's all take a walk. Many of these games can be played while two are walking. Unless they are in the mood for other sorts. Ghosts can even be played in an automobile, or on a boat.

AUTANTONYMS

In open country, if we walk too fast, we may heedlessly get caught fast in a trap. If we escape that and come to a lake, we may see that a boat is fast at the dock or loose, and perhaps going fast; but we should always remember that a fast woman *is* loose.

It all depends. To dress a chicken, for example, we may remove the feathers or put on feathers, depending on whether we expect to eat it or to feed it. To loose is the same as to unloose; bend as unbend; annul as disannul; ravel as unravel. Shameful and shameless are at least sin—pardon me—synonyms.

To carry on may mean to behave normally, or to behave abnormally, as when the teacher leaves the room.

English owns a numbers of such autantonyms, words that mean their own opposite.

Players are to write as many autantonyms as they can think of in three minutes. Then the one with most words begins: for each word he gives sentences illustrating its two meanings.

IRREVERSIBLES

To *stand under* a shower, you need not *understand* the principles of falling water. You may *speak out* your opinion without being able to *outspeak* those that disagree. Such expressions are Irreversibles.

"Irreversible" is a term in mathematics. In simple arithmetic, addition and multiplication are reversible: 3 times 4 equals 4 times 3. Subtraction and division are not. Yet in higher mathematics I understand—that's the wrong word: I have read but I do not understand—there are cases where a times b is not the same as b times a.

However, I have pondered the case of three boys to eat four ice cream cones: how much for each boy? Here surely is no simple case! We must not merely divide; we must ask the age of the boys, who is paying for the cones, and what in farm language is called the pecking order. But the question soars into extraterrestrial considerations if we ask about three ice cream cones to eat four boys. Such items, on this planet, are irreversible.

Irreversibles are mainly the over and under words, and the ins and outs. For example:

inborn—born in; inhere—herein; outlay—lay out; downright—right down; outgrow—grow out; overact—act over; oversee—see over; withdraw—draw with; income—come in; outreach—reach out; outjump—jump out; undertake—take under; overdo—do over; overtake—take over; overpay—pay over; overwork—work over; overreach—reach over; withstand—stand with; in step—instep—step in; output—put out; outboard—board out; overhang—hangover—hang over; overrun—run over; overall—all over; overthrow—throw over; inroads—roads in; outcome—come out; outright—right out; outdo—do out; outlive—live out; overrule—rule over; oversee—see over; overtime—time over

There may be various degrees of association between the two members of an irreversible pair. Some, while usually different, may be used so as to have about the same significance; you may say "Come out and play" or ask: "How did things come out?

What was the outcome?" Some may be used in almost opposite senses, as when you look over a paper to correct it, or overlook the paper in the batch handed in. Or there may be only an accidental relation of form, as when inure is reversed and we have urine. These possibilities add unexpected turns to the Game.

Players write as many irreversibles as they can think of in three minutes. Then each in turn gives two sentences, using the two reversed terms in their different senses.

In the case of words that, when they turnabout, break apart, the sentence may separate the two parts. Thus you may wonder whether the *night* will ever be *over;* someone may complain that they tried to *do* him *out* of a job; or, if there is *time* left *over,* you may suggest some other game to keep the folk busy.

Variation

Player gives a sentence, using one form of an Irreversible. Then he points. Player pointed at must at once give a sentence using the reversed form of the word. Then this player gives a sentence with another Irreversible, and points to another player. Sentences must be appropriate and should be amusing.

ALLWAYS

Not quite the same as the family of Irreversibles, but with the same sort of complications, is the *all* family. Some members of the family exist in pairs: already—all ready; always—all ways; altogether—all together. But there is no partner for all right. This word, if I may call it such, is always two words. On the other hand, although, almost, also always stand as one.

Young folk still fresh with wonder at the wonder of words (a freshness that in some is sempiternal) may make a game of the *All* words. Each player is to write six sentences, making proper use of the terms in the three pairs above—one word joined, with a single *L*—the other, two words with double *L*. The group decides which sentences are most entertaining. Of course, check to see that each word is correctly used. It is altogether desirable that words always be correctly used, so that they are all right.

5

Rhymes and Jinglings

Pope lisped in numbers, for the numbers came. He did not mean mathematics. To versify is not difficult; most anyone vatic can (though this Pope was not of the Vatican). For in truth, rhyme came before reason. Poetry came before science. Poetry is man's leap; science, his landing.

Primitive man both punned and rhymed. It was the sophisticated Greeks (whom the Romans copied) that moved on from rhyme, as later, in English, blank verse grew out of the jingles. But always, as a pig or a poet to his pen, as a fool to his folly, our tongues return upon a rhyme.

There are many rhyming games. An early one, known from the French as BOUTS-RIMÉS, which builds lines from assigned words, tag-ends of rhyme, has been a favorite in many countries and times. In eighteenth century England, at Bath and other resorts, it was as popular as today's card games.

Assign players two pairs of rhyming words, the same to all. They are to build stanzas ending with these words, in any order. The words may be used in one stanza, or two. Group decides which are most effective.

For example: pen-scuffle-men-ruffle; girl-glisten-swirl-listen. Try to select humorous possibilities: rover-halfseas over; wary-

merry-constabulary-vocabulary. Your vocabulary can be sup-
plemented through rhyming dictionaries, several of which are in
circulation, for poetasters, writers of Christmas cards, and con-
cocters of commercials.

RHYMIT

Give all the players the same four words, which do not rhyme.
They are to write stanzas, of two or four lines each, rhyming
these words. The stanzas need not be all in one poem, but they
should make good sense or good nonsense. Group decides which
are the most effective. Here are some words that have led to
amusing stanzas:

recallable, orgy, critics, wants, replenish, lounging, slowpoke,
puss, engine, owlet, ogler, obesity, lentil, spoilt, eagerly, python,
toilet, respectable, stoppage, flimflam, pints, litany, frosty, vol-
cano, oblige, barbiturate, gossip, title, nitric, anklet, fez, thought-
less, widow, flimsy, luscious, pontiff, rescue, starve, polarize,
morbid, exhaust, orange, bozo, warble, impish, iris, sauce,
crepuscular, swordsman, nautch, rainbow

Some of these words have a natural rhyme, as crepuscular-
muscular, flimsy-whimsy. Others can be rhymed by linking them
to pairs or parts of words, as litany-hit any; nitric-sly trick;
anklet- will the bank let . . . Tinkle along!

CENTO

Each player writes a line from a poem. No just made-up lines
are allowed; a player must be able to identify the source of his
quotation.

Papers are passed to the right, and each player writes a line
from another poem, that in some way fits what he finds on the
sheet now before him. Continue for two more lines; the fourth
line must rhyme with one of the others.

Players must have in mind a goodly store of diversified lines.
Here is a cento merrily mixed:

It was a friar of orders grey,
Still harping on my daughter.
Sister spirit come away,
But don't go near the water.

and here one lugubrious!

The youngest of the sister arts
Was born upon the open sea,
The rest were slain at Chevy Chase
And Oh! the difference to me.

FILQUOTE

Read aloud a fairly well-known passage of poetry, BUT stop before the last line. Allow time for the players to write down, as well as they can recollect it, the last line of the passage. Then read the next. Player with the most correct wins.

Here are a few suggested passages. Do not read the line in parenthesis.

1. Vice is a monster of so frightful mien
(As to be hated, needs but to be seen.) *Alexander Pope*

2. Fair daffodills, we weep to see
You haste away so soon;
As yet the early-rising sun
(Has not attained his noon.) *Robert Herrick*

3. Hail to thee, blithe spirit!
Bird thou never wert,
That from heaven, or near it,
Pourest thy full heart
(In profuse strains of unpremeditated art.)

Percy Bysshe Shelley

4. Souls of poets dead and gone,
What Elysium have ye known,
Happy field or mossy cavern
(Choicer than the Mermaid Tavern?) *John Keats*

5. The curfew tolls the knell of parting day,
The lowing herd winds slowly o'er the lea,
The ploughman homeward plods his weary way,
(And leaves the world to darkness, and to me.)   *Thomas Gray*

6. Lord God of hosts, be with us yet,
(Lest we forget, lest we forget.)   *Rudyard Kipling*

7. Fat black bucks in a wine-barrel room,
Barrel-house kings, with feet unstable,
Sagged and reeled and pounded on the table,
Pounded on the table,
Beat an empty barrel with the handle of a broom,
Hard as they were able,
(Boom, boom, BOOM.)   *Vachel Lindsay*

8. Or in the night, imagining some fear,
(How easy is a bush supposed a bear.)   *William Shakespeare*

9. Grow old along with me,
The best is yet to be,
(The last of life, for which the first was made.)
                                        Robert Browning

Any anthology will provide many more of these. A handy one
is Francis T. Palgrave's *Golden Treasury*. To the Mentor
paperback printing of this, Oscar Williams has added poems
from Palgrave's time to our own.

Variation

For a more poetic couple or group, here's a trickier play. First
person gives the first line of a stanza or poem; next must respond
with the last line. The second person then gives another first
line, for which the last line must be supplied. The one that can
supply most last lines wins. If a large group is playing, those
unable to give the last line drop out, until only one survives.
The host or other person should be selected in advance as referee, to decide whether the first line is from too obscure a poem;
if it is, the speaker must select another. For example:

When to the sessions of sweet silent thought . . .
All losses are restored, and sorrows end.

Shall I compare thee to a summer's day? . . .
So long lives this, and this gives life to thee.

I wandered lonely as a cloud . . .
And dances with the daffodils.

Once upon a midnight dreary . . .
Shall be lifted nevermore.

Come live with me and be my love . . .
Then live with me and be my love.

RHYMORIGINALS

Dictate a line you have made up. Players are to use this in a four line stanza, which they have five minutes to fashion. The group decides which is most effective.

Try to select lines with sentimental or humorous possibilities. Here are some that have worked well:

She looked across the road, and then . . .
His heart had skipped a beat, for all at once . . .
Under the lindens, when the sun was low . . .
The spaceship wavered, caught between two stars . . .
Four little troglodytes, romping in the subway . . .
The summer sun was setting. Underneath . . .

Variations

1. You may give each player a different line, and listen to the varied results.

2. Instead of assigning a line, assign a subject. For instance—woman rules; evening in autumn; 1996; the missing glove.

TRANSRHYME

First player gives a sentence. Next player must give another sentence promptly—beginning with a word that rhymes with the last word of the sentence just given. Next player must do the same, and so on.

Anyone that cannot start with a rhyme in 15 seconds drops out, and the next player rhymes it. If no one can give a rhyming sentence, all that are in stay in, that word is bypassed, and another sentence is given by the person that gave the unrhymable one. Continue until one player is left. The game might proceed somewhat like this:

I was thinking of dropping in to see you last Sunday.
Gun day, you should call it. I was out hunting.
Bunting was better for me. I played baseball, and that's how we brought in the winning run.
One of you . . .

   And so it may run along. Or:

I'm thinking of going.
Rowing is good exercise.
Eyes front!
Hunt for the needle in the haystack.
Say, stack your cards in a better pack.
Rack your brains for something funny.
Honey, will you get me some candy?
Dandy! Then we'll be quits!
Wits are what you need for this sort of thing.
Ring around a rosy.
Those elude my memory; I'm not good at rhymes.
Crimes! What crimes are committed in the name of verse!

   If the company is well enough equipped, you may rule that, instead of original sentences, all the rhymes must be made of a well known saying, a proverb, a line from a poem or other famous quotation. (The words *a, an, and, the* may be disregarded, if they come before the rhyme.) A series might then go on like this:

Sorrows remembered sweeten present joy.
The boy stood on the burning deck, whence all but he had fled.
And shed a bitter tear.
Fear no more the heat o' the sun.
One and God make a majority.

Do the growing-up generation qualify for this kind of game?

LIMERICKSAW

Few persons need an introduction to the limerick. Dictate a line you make up. Give the players five minutes to make a limerick beginning with that line. The group selects the most effective.

Here are some lines that have gotten players into complications:

With a handful of ten-dollar bills . . .
With some wine that had grown rather musty . . .
A girl who delighted to flirt . . .
There was a young girl named McGillicuddy . . .

And here are a few noted limericks:

> For beauty I am not a star.
> There are others more handsome by far.
> But my face, I don't mind it,
> Because I'm behind it;
> It's the fellow in front gets the jar!

> There was a young fellow named Bright
> Who traveled more quickly than light.
> He went out one day
> In a relative way
> And returned on the previous night.

> A curious bird is the pelican,
> His bill can hold more than his belly can.
> He can put in his beak
> Enough for a week
> And I'm bothered to know how the hell he can.

> A fly and a flea in a flue
> Were imprisoned, so what could they do?
> Said the fly: "Let us flee!"
> Said the flea: "Let us fly!"
> So they flew through a flaw in the flue.

> There was a young lady of Lynn
> Who was so uncommonly thin

That when she essayed
To drink lemonade
She slipped through the straw and fell in.

There once was a man from Nantucket
Who kept all his cash in a bucket,
But his daughter, named Nan,
Ran away with a man,
And as for the bucket, Nantucket.

But he followed the pair to Pawtucket—
The man and the girl with the bucket;
And he said to the man
"You are welcome to Nan"—
But as for the bucket, Pawtucket.

Then the pair followed Paw to Manhasset
Where he still held the cash as an asset;
But Nan and the man
Stole the money and ran,
And as for the bucket, Manhasset.

LIMERICKUT

At the end of his bright anthology *Out on a Limerick,* Bennett
Cerf introduces a new type he calls "beheaded limericks," in-
stancing five by a Mrs. Shaw of New Orleans. These build the
pattern by breaking a word in half in each line, and setting the
first half at the line-end as the rhyme. One set of Mrs. Shaw's
beheadings runs:

> A certain young pate who was addle
> Rode a horse he alleged to be saddle.
> But his gust which was dis
> For his haps which were mis
> Sent him back to his lac which was Cadil.

Cerf's book ends with the challenge: "If you think they're easy
to invent, just try one yourself!" So I came out of my shower
dripping this one:

> An expert in culture that's horti
> Though lacking in tude that is forti,

With no vy that is en,
And no sor that is cen,
Took up with a san that is courte.

Next night, while waiting for the curtain to rise on the delightful
City Center Ballet, it struck me that in Mrs. Shaw's limerickut
(and my own) there is a lamentable monotony, each line bump-
ing to its rhyme with an apologetic "that was," "which were,"
"that is." And I wondered why, at least in the two short lines,
the decapitated limericks might not have Madame Guillotine
slice a word like a worm so that it moves off in two directions.

In two intermissions, therefore, I jotted down two limerickuts.
I copy them from my ballet program:

A fellow quite ky that is chun
Was riding a key that is don,
When a nut from the wall
Hit the guy for a fall,
And he swore at the key that is mon.

With a fair smiling ture that is den,
Regardless of sure that is cen,
Shall he soo for the lass
Or try key for a pass?
No gain, if no ture that is ven.

In each of these, in addition to the double use of wallnut, fall-
guy, lassoo (sue), and passkey, the central syllables in the three
long lines have the same sound. Other variations can probably
be wrung, such as double-meanings for the decollated words in
the long lines. No swimmer or free swinger of limericks should
drown in the Cerf!

RHYMING SLANG

The British have developed an indirect sort of slang, which
substitutes a rhyme for the word in mind. Thus, in "Pass the
Aristotle" the last word, as you have guessed, stands for bottle.

By far the greater number of such expressions substitute not
a word but a phrase. He's gone into the soup and gravy—the

Navy. He's gone out for saint and sinner—dinner. He's at the near 'n' far—bar. He's in the off 'n' on—John (toilet).

A few of these expressions have come into general use, even in the less readily rhyming United States. In "Let's get down to brass tacks," brass tacks is rhyming slang for facts.

The process of substitution did not stop with rhyme. In clipped speech, the actual rhyming word is omitted. Only the first part of the phrase is spoken; the rhyme and the word in mind are both assumed. Thus "my china" means my friend: china plate—mate. It's up the apples (and pears)—stairs. He's on his pat (Malone)—own. Sometimes the allusion is quite far-fetched. Thus "Not on your Nellie!" means "not on your life!" The journey is—Nellie Duff—puff—last puff—breath of life.

Probably few that refer to money as sugar, or speak of some-body's sugar-daddy, know that this too is rhyming slang. Of the three first words that were rhyming slang for money—bees and honey; bread and honey; sugar and honey, because of its sweet association sugar has survived.

In America, rhyming slang followed a different path, favoring not substitution but repetition of sound. Such phrases as eager beaver, cheerful earful, the bee's knees, sweep into popular favor and as quickly out again. As early as bidding the baby: come sit on pappy's lappy. Don't let this make you slap-happy . . . has "punch drunk" any connection with the emptied bowl?

Rhyming slang sounds as though the vagabond poet Villon should have used it, but the first literary reference to it is in *The Mysteries of London,* a melodrama written in 1846 by the once enormously popular but now almost forgotten William MacArthur Reynolds. Once started, rhyming slang caught on like wildfire. (Ever see a wildfire? I did, on stage in the melodrama *Engine 999.*) Soon it developed the subtler shadings I have indi-cated; for strong as man's urge to communicate is his desire to be understood by but a chosen few. The exoteric and the esoteric impulse are as a man's two cortices. His right works hard on interlingua and basic English to spread understanding across the world, while with equal though more individual fervor his left toils to fashion *Finnegans Wake* and other towers of force to let babble once more loose upon the lands. It's all a bloody (rhyming slang—shame-game). It's part of the spirit of play that man carries from babyhood through all his years, sensing the truth of the poet's dictum that "genius is wisdom—and youth."

Groups, families, even paired pals, have developed more personal and private patterns of rhyming slang. Sometimes a rhyme-substitute may be a treasured family preserve, as when "time to tread!" prods the youngsters to ask—"Mayn't I stay up just a little longer?" No doubt you can recall such rhyming slang creations of your own—or can fashion new ones. I have no more to bread on the subject. Do you follow me? Then this is all I shall honor. (Bread and butter . . . utter; honor bright . . . write.)

RHYMING SLANGUAGE

First player speaks a sentence of which one word is the un-rhyming part of a rhyme-phrase substitute for the word in his mind. Next player must complete the phrase and name the intended word. Then he gives a similar sentence, and the next player must solve it. Anyone failing to solve the sentence given him drops out. (A chosen referee will interrupt if he thinks the substitute is too far fetched; then the one that gave it drops out.) The game goes on until only one player is left, or it's a jolly tie, like a tennis match that never gets beyond deuce.

A round of Rhyming Slanguage might go:

1. If you tell me your secret, I won't bread a word of it.
2. Bread and butter, the word is utter.
    I'll go to your aunt's if you'll honor me a word of introduction.
3. Honor bright, the word is write.
    Don't mince to me; I can see right through you.
4. Mince pie, the word is lie.
    Your hair is bright today; did it get that way in the water?
5. Bright and early, the word is curly.

Your eyes are thunder; are you pleased with what he said?
6. Thunder and Lightning, the word is brightening.

On my next power, I'm wondering whether to go by boat or plane.
7. Power of attorney, the word is journey.

Here are some other words used in rhyming slang, with their meaning:

Boat (boat race)—used to mean face
bird (. . . lime)—time
burnt (. . . cinder)—window
butchers (. . . hook)—look. Take a butchers at her!
pigs (. . . ear)—beer
dicky (. . . bird)—word
lakes (. . . of Killarney)—barmy. "He's lakes!" is, alas, a frequently expressed opinion.
twist (. . . and twirl)—girl. "Some twist, eh?" as a pretty one passes.

It is not hard to make up more rhyming slang. It is not hard, indeed, to make rhymed verse, or for that matter blank verse, or free verse. The hard thing to make up is poetry.

6

Anagrammateasing

Of all classes of word games, the several sorts of anagrams have been lengthily and consistently the most often played. Simply, to anagrammatize is to transpose the letters of a word so as to form another word or other words.

Anagrams were first composed of names. With *i* and *j* formerly interchangeable, also *u* and *v,* John Bunyan wrote in his "Holy War" (1682):

> Witness my name, if anagram'd to thee,
> The letters make 'Nu hony in a B'.

Young Arouet (Junior: *Le Jeune*) over in France added the initials *l j* to his name, and thenceforth became known to the world as Voltaire. Followers of the English statesman Disraeli produced the anagram of his name—I lead, Sir. Thereupon his opponents published another anagram: Idle airs. Eleanor Davies, in the time of the Stuart kings, claimed to be a prophetess, putting forward as evidence the anagram of her name—Reveal, O Daniel! But the Court of High Commission disposed of Dame Eleanor Davies with the returned anagram—Never soe mad a ladie! Lewis Carroll devised two anagrams for the statesman William Ewart Gladstone:

Wilt tear down all images?
Wild agitator! Means well.

Here are a few anagrams of other noted persons, to figure out
and pass along:

Anagram	Number of Names	Person
1. More clover, Will	2	10. Oliver Goldsmith
2. We praise him; all sake	2	9. Leonidas
3. I tear bent lines	2	8. Thucydides
4. Alien do feed	2	7. Michael Angelo
5. I led U C	1	6. Gainsborough
6. O go hug brains	1	5. Euclid
7. Each a mile long	2	4. Daniel Defoe
8. I decyd thus	1	3. Albert Einstein
9. No ladies	1	2. William Shakespeare
10. Dig over Toms hill	2	1. Oliver Cromwell

ANATREES

Dictate the following passage. Then tell the players which
words to underline. Announce that these words are anagrams for
trees. The one that identifies all the trees first wins.

You can make this harder by not telling which words to underline. Just announce that 20 trees are hidden in the passage, and
let the players hunt. Here is the passage:

In a cabin a *mile north* on the River *Wye,* lives old *Lem* with
his pet *lamb.* Old rags take the place of window *panes* and door
panel. Possessed of *ample* means, he *has* not *cared* to wear other
covering than a ragged *dolman,* nor to drink from any but a
cheap blue *mug.* At night he goes to *reap* the harvest of his
melon patch. He will *take* a *lamp* in one hand to *allure* insects,
and a *lump* of *rock* in the other with which to slay a possible
weasel.

And here, in order, are the 20 trees: lime, thorn, yew, elm, balm,
aspen, plane, maple, ash, cedar, almond, peach, gum, pear,
lemon, teak, palm, laurel, plum, cork.

Sometimes a whole sentence can be amusingly anagramma-teased. For instance, "Dangers of amateur physicking" transposes into the warning—"The sick men pay for drugs again!" This sort of anagram takes more time to devise than to convert, or vice versa.

APTAGRAMS

See what you can do with these, then try them on your friends. They are Aptagrams—the scramble in some way fits the original word.

1. Lo! I dress
2. Go nurse!
3. great helps
4. rare mad frolic (2 words)
5. I cry that I sin
6. comic trade
7. neat leg
8. real fun
9. Tim in a pet
10. into my arm
11. mind his map
12. reap sad toils (2 words)
13. Nay, I repent it
14. no more stars
15. ten teapots
16. best in prayer
17. rash games in Paris (2 words)
18. there we sat
19. guess a fearful ruin (2 words)
20. lures for me
21. every cent paid me (2 words)
22. O sour hope!

22. poorhouse
21. received payment
20. remorseful
19. universal suffrage
18. sweetheart
17. Spanish marriages
16. Presbyterian
15. potentates
14. astronomers
13. penitentiary
12. Paradise Lost
11. midshipman
10. matrimony
9. impatient
8. funeral
7. elegant
6. democratic
5. Christianity
4. radical reform
3. telegraphs
2. surgeon
1. soldiers

ANACLUES

Sometimes you can enliven a spell of anagrams by having the players mind their cues as well as their P's.

Dictate the anagrams; allow two minutes for players to guess the other words. Then all who have any words figured out show them to you. Give them ten points for each word right.

Then give the clues. As soon as one player has all figured out, stop the play. He gets ten points. Now score five points for each word right (not given ten points before). Highest score wins.

You can easily make clues for any of the anagrams in the game above. Make the clue tricky, or just give a synonym. Here are a few samples:

Anagram	Clue	Word
1. lady mine	what an unmarried woman should be	5. astronomers
2. city life	bliss	4. lawyers
3. to run at men	tilting	3. tournament
4. sly ware	That's what their clients think	2. felicity
5. moon-starers	That's as they seem to laymen	1. maidenly

SCRAMBLEGRAMS

Most anagrammatists do not trouble to find real words formed by the letters of the base word, but are content to make a meaningless scramble of its letters, to be reconverted. Here are some scramblefied cities of the United States; to how many of them have you been? Ask your friends.

1. ccaghio	8. Honolulu
2. bnotos	7. Cincinnati
3. aabynl	6. Detroit
4. ttsgrbuip	5. Cleveland
5. leledncva	4. Pittsburg
6. ttdrioe	3. Albany
7. cciiinnnta	2. Boston
8. nulluoho	1. Chicago

And here are a few places you and your friends may like to visit:

1. also	8. Indonesia
2. aims	7. Spain
3. aprise	6. Oman
4. dean	5. Denmark
5. darkmen	4. Aden
6. moan	3. Persia
7. pains	2. Siam
8. sad one I in	1. Laos

ANACOUPLE

Instead of scrambling one word, mix up a pair that usually go together. Prepare a clue. Players are to find the two linked words in the Anacouple. For example: cdyvsplleeeiiar. Clue—hurried and guarded arrival. Pair—special delivery. Here are a few other couples you may scramble, and attach to clues:

Carnegie Hall; Christmas Eve; plum pudding; screen test; New Years; hydrogen bomb; United Nations; post office; scrambled eggs; swan song; apple pie; mince meat; hot chocolate; ice cream; cream puff; battle cry

Variation A

Scramble only half of a pair. Players are to figure it out, and write *the other half of the pair*. First to get all right wins.

You give:	*Players write*	*Words*
1. tteurb	5. Little Bo Peep	lost her sheep
2. poetaarlc	4. cabbage	corned beef
3. tliuje	3. Romeo	Juliet
4. froecebnde (2 words)	2. Antony	Cleopatra
5. sspreehthole (3 words)	1. bread	butter

Other couplings that may be scrambled, either as a whole or just one half, are:

hustle-bustle; thunder-lightning; fine-dandy; cigars-cigarettes; sugar-cream; horse-buggy; milk-honey; Hero-Leander; Samson-Delilah; David-Goliath; Punch-Judy; Jack-Jill; Adam-Eve; Roland-Oliver; Abelard-Heloise; Aucassin-Nicolette; Tristan-Isolde; Beatrice-Benedick; Romulus-Remus; Damon-Pythias; bricks-without straw; Barkis-is willing; Tower-of Babel; Lochin-var-out of the west; barmecide-feast (empty dishes); bachelor's-fare (bread and cheese and kisses)

Variation B

Give each player a piece of paper with a scramble on it, the first part of a pair. Each player is to have a different scramble. Player must solve his scramble, and figure out the second part of the pair. He folds under the first scramble, and now makes a scramble of the second part of the pair. Papers are then exchanged.

On his new sheet, each player figures out the new scramble, and writes what he thinks is the *first part* of the pair.

Players in turn read their final word; then open the paper and see whether it fits the original scramble on the sheet. Often an amusing change will have taken place. (Either half of the pair may be given as the first scramble. Thus in the words under Variation A, Cleopatra is scrambled, though the play is named, and we usually say, Antony and Cleopatra. (Ladies first in an emergency!)

Scrambled Place Cards:

For an amusing minute before a meal, instead of writing the names of your guests on the place cards, set down a scramble-gram of the name. There will be lots of laughter as your guests go around the table trying to identify themselves.

The easiest, and perhaps the most frequent variety of anagrams consists in giving the players a long word, and three minutes. They are to make as many words as they can, using only the letters of the base word. In any word they make, no letter can be used more times than it occurs in the base word.

Select a word related to the occasion, as shamrock, Christmas; or to a person in the party, as jockey, advertise; or use the name of a guest, as Percival, Silverstone. One variety of this game, using letters instead of a base word, can be called

ANASCALE

Tell players to write down the letters of the musical scale: A, B, C, D, E, F, G. Dictate clues. The one that gets all the words first wins. For instance:

Clue	Word
1. human countenance	10. café
2. top card	9. beg
3. old exclamation	8. Abe
4. moment's vogue	7. bed
5. given to eat	6. cab
6. vehicle	5. fed
7. sleeping place	4. fad
8. Lincoln	3. gad, egad
9. petition	2. ace
10. eating place	1. face

Other words from the scale—make the clues yourself—include —dab, gab, bad, bead, bag, fade, bade, badge, cage, deaf, dace.

Here is a short list of words that can break up into a goodly supply of smaller words:

composer, disgraceful, tormenting, counterplot, separate, swathe, mindless, duplicate, timeworn, poniard, dromedary, defiant, porcelain, shackle, lonesome, thundering, careworn

Give any of these; allow five minutes for the players to see how many words they can form from them.

Variation

Pick a number of words contained in the base word, and make clues for them. Perhaps you can use as base word the name of your chief guest, or a word associated with him. Have the players write the base word, and the clues as you dictate them. Then they must guess the words; first one finished wins.

Here is an octet used on television. By getting all eight correct, Thomas J. Kane of Lockport, New York, answered the $64,000 question. That's $8,000 a word. How many can you get? The letters are all in the name Eisenhower.

1. smallest of the mammals	8. herse
2. an evening party	7. seine
3. a willow whose flexible twigs are used for furniture	6. ewers
4. short title of a Utopian novel	5. hieron
5. generic term for Greek temple	4. Erewhon
6. plural for a wide mouth pitcher	3. osier
7. a large net for fishing	2. soiree
8. a frame on which skins are dried, as for parchment	1. shrew

Variation, Sentengrams

Players are to form sentences out of words they fashion from a base word. Allow five minutes. The best way to play is to use half the time making words from the base word. Then combine them into sentences. Let us suppose the base word is TURNSTILE. Make your preliminary list of words. Then sentences may be formed, such as:

Let runts enlist. Let unlit suet rest in utensil. Let sunlit litter stir lustre. Turn stunt sitter in urn. Sire, set nest in sunlit site.

Score: For most sentences, ten points. For each sentence, five points. For every word more than four in a sentence, two points. For every letter more than five in a word, two points. For wrong word, two points off. Highest score wins.

Variation, Anablank

Choose a base word, and with the words you have found in it, plus other words, make sentences. Give players the base word.

Dictate the sentences, BUT instead of giving the words from the base word, say *blank* and give the number of letters in that word. First to fit in the right words wins.

Suppose your base word is SHAPELIER. (This allows you to have two e's in a word.) Your sentences might then run like this:

The — 6 hurried to save the — 5, lest it suffer a — 7 and — 6. He was — 5 than his — 4, though an early — 5. He kept his — 5 dog on a — 5; his wife told him she always — 4 — 4 when it seems to — 6 grubbing in garbage — 5. Let us — 5 this impression, and tell the truth, so as not to make a — 4 out of the — 6. Who will — 5 when they — 5 the — 5? — 5 no effort to — 6 any contrary regulations. — 4 and farewell! And don't be — 4!

This may seem hard, but once you get a few words, the rest fall into the pattern. Go quickly along, setting down the words that first occur to you. The idea will begin to shine through. Then go back and work on the other words. Here, in order, are the words for the blanks—healer, sheep, relapse, perish, paler, pals, riser, sheep, leash, raps, hers, relish, pails, erase, liar, healer, share, shear, sheep, spare, repeal, hail, rash.

Other good base words for Anablank are patience, courage, fortune, marriage, incandescent, glorified.

SLYGRAMS

Take a few lines from a not too well known passage of verse or prose, and scramble the key words in them. Write the passage, with the scrambles, on a sheet for each player expected, or put the whole on a card large enough for all to see when you hold it up for them to copy. The one that gets the words reconverted first wins. Here is a verse Slygram:

> Leos eugjd of truth, in endless rrroe druehl,
> The rgyol, stej, and derdli of the drowl.

And here is a Slygram in prose:

We are told that the vledi is the raheft of sile, and was a liar from the niningebg; so that, ydoneb contradiction, the nonen-

tivi is old; and, which is rome, his first yessa of it was purely
clapiliot, employed in inninugremd the authority of his encpir,
and gesidunc a third part of the cujbests from their codeebeni;
for which he was driven down morf vanehe.

The scrambled words in the two passages above, in order, are
—sole judge, error hurled, glory, jest, riddle, world, devil,
father, lies, beginning, beyond, invention, more, essay, political,
undermining, prince, seducing, subjects, obedience, from
heaven.

It is not difficult to make your own Slygrams.

Variation, Slyblanks

Take any not too well known passage of poetry or prose. Take
out the key words; scramble them, and put them at the bottom,
in a mixed order, leaving blanks in the passage. Dictate the passage, then the scrambles. First to put them into their proper
places, converted, wins. Here's a slyblank that cannot be familiar, because I just made it up:

When she — the sun was — high. It is — she could
not — it very well through the — of the forest trees, but the
sunbeams cast a golden — around, beyond the forest.
        remhims, kawoe, reut, ese, hercansb, dyalare

Here are the converted words, in the correct order, but spelled
backwards: ekowa, ydaerla, eurt, ees, sehcnarb, remmihs

You can of course make Slyblanks as simple or as difficult as
you desire.

ANAGRADDS

Here is a form of anagrams that gives greater scope; it calls
for more ingenuity.

Give all the players the same base word. They are to set down
as many words as they can, of four or more letters, using only
letters in the base word, BUT any letter may be used any number of times in each new word. Tell them that longer words score
more.

Try this, for a moment, with the word WRITE. You can get twit, twitter, rewrite, triter, wire, rite, wetter, and many more.

Score: five for the most words. Two points for each word. For every letter more than five in a word, one point. Highest score wins.

Other words that might be used for Anagradds are:

gleam, bounced, drought, drove, kindle, elapse, edict, impose, tonic. Note that tonic gives you the *ion* ending, as in concoction. Once you get "the hang" of this type of word-forming, it can be lively.

TIEGRAMS

The simplest form of the anagram variety I call Tiegrams is to give the players several scrambled words so that, when they convert them and set them in proper order, their first letters also spell a word. Suppose you give them tggiinnhl, leistarve, stteeor, arreeil, ptenroupo, ravelec. They should convert these into lightning, versatile, rosette, earlier, opportune, cleaver. These words can be set so that their first letters spell clover.

Tiegrams are easy to fashion; just start with the first-letter word; put after each letter a word beginning with that letter, then scramble these words and their order. Here is a Tiegram you can use when you expect a LAWYER:

tiludeey, aaadiefots, ddooeotmnar, snoreymealey, gnewheyilz, niiittogal. Those scrambles convert into Yuletide, asafoetida, rodomontade, eleemosynary, wheezingly, litigation; these words can be rearranged so that the first letters spell lawyer.

Variation, Tieclues

Dictate not scrambles, but a clue to each of a series of words, plus the number of letters in the word. Players can check whether they have the right words, because if they are right, the words can be so arranged that their first letters will spell another word. For instance:

Clue	Letters	Word (*backwards*)
1. all the undies	8	9. ebordraw
2. fine woven fabric	4	8. lwahs
3. shortest hose	7	7. taocrevo
4. sign of betrothal	14 (2 words)	6. yreisoh
5. paired pendants	8	5. sgnirrae
6. then the shoes	7	4. gnir tnemegagne
7. when it's colder	8	3. stelkna
8. for the shoulders or head	5	2. ecal
9. includes all the rest	8	1. eiregnil

First letter clue: in large quantities . . . elaselohw

Let's make a trickier one. Take the word MURINE, meaning mouselike. Here are possible developments:

Clue	Letters	Word
1. has a lot to learn	8	6. intestate
2. not to be tossed out of sight	7	5. umbilical
3. quiet for the morning grass	10	4. mastodon
4. once was a big fellow	8	3. roriferous
5. tie mother hates to lose	9	2. eyeball
6. how no millionaire should go	9	1. neophyte

First letters clue: the submissive husband

Dictate the clues to your best-worded friends, and you'll have a free quarter-hour to get the sandwiches ready.

DOUBLE TIEGRAMS

Give players two words that are linked in idea, and have the same number of letters. They are to write these side by side down the sheet, one letter under the other. Next to each pair of letters, they are to write as many words as they can, beginning with the first letter on that line, and ending with the other letter. Allow three minutes; the one with most words—but at least one for every line—wins.

Thus you might suggest:

Pair	Some words players might find:
E . . . C	emetic
N . . . H	nigh, nargileh
G . . . A	gondola, gladiola
L . . . N	London, linen, limn
I . . . N	Iberian, ion, inaction
S . . . E	slave, snare
H . . . L	heel, heal, hell

If there seem to be words enough, you might specify the number of letters in the words. Thus, for the following, only four-letter words:

B . . . B	bulb, boob, bomb
L . . . R	leer, liar, lair, Lear
A . . . O	also, alto
C . . . W	claw, craw, crow, chow, chew
K . . . N	keen, kiln

The one that has most words—but at least one for every line—wins.

It may happen that one of your expected guests has a first and a last name with the same number of letters. Give these for the players to set down, and see how many words they can fit between. Thus:

F . . . C	frantic, fanatic
R . . . A	radiola, Rama, regalia, razzia
A . . . L	assail, avail, all, ail, annual
N . . . H	nigh, nargileh, neigh
C . . . O	curio, Chicago
E . . . U	emu
S . . . N	sensation, son, scion, scintillation

These have come to me at first thought; there are probably many more. You can use any equally lettered pair, and make your own tiegrams.

MULTANAGRAMS

A more complicated form of anagram is that in which, say, four words are given that, by properly distributing their letters, can be rearranged as four other words. Thus:

Given words	*Clue to anagrams*	*Letters in new words*
chronic	turned about	8
adversity	nagging	8
wholesome	weaving machines	5
cuss	perishability	8

The multanagram breaks into—converse, shrewish, looms, caducity.

Multanagrams are not hard to make. I formed the one above in three minutes flat (though the last word is perhaps a breath off key. You can belike do better). I took the first three words that popped into my head. From them, I formed *converse* and *shrewish*. I then needed an extra *s,* and had left over the letters c-a-d-i-t-y-o-l-o-m. A little thought gave me the last word on my first list, to form the two more on my second. Try to form some multanagrams, or get your friends to. They are as much fun to fashion as to solve.

All good roads lead home, and here we are back again at the true anagram, one of a pair or more of words using the same letters. Twist all the letters around, and shape other words. Thus: scrape—capers; limped—dimple; sward—wards—draws; enters —tenser—resent—rest, en; depart—parted—apt (pat), red; porter—report—tor (ort), rep; master—stream—set, ram; steals—slates—set, sal; slave—vales—salve—veals—laves; live —evil—levi—veil—vile; pots—stop—tops—spot—post; onset —notes—tones—stone—so, net (ten); idolatry—dilatory— adroitly—tail, dory—toil, dray; aspired—praised—despair— per, dais—sire, pad—pier, sad—spar, die—par, dies—spear (spare), id; pares—pears—reaps—spare—parse—spear—rapes —asper—prase—asp (sap), re; lair—liar—rail; peat—tape— pate; stare—tares—rates—tears; sear—eras—arse—rase—ears; cruet—truce—recut—cuter;   times—items—smite—mites— emits—me, its; relay—layer—early; result—sutler—lustre—

ulster—rustle—rulest—lurest; cats—scat—acts—cast; tables—
stable—bleats—ablest—be, last; nest—sent—nets—tens; slate
—stale—steal—least—tales; trope—toper—retop—porte; shear
—share—hears—hares — re, has; priest—stripe—sprite—ripest
—esprit—tripes; bared—beard—brade—bread—debar; acres—
races—cares—scare—sacre; education—cautioned—auctioned

TWISTAGRAMS

Allow players three minutes to write as many twistagrams as
they can. There must be at least two in each set.

Score—for every word no one else has, ten points. For every
word more than two in a group, two points. For every word of
more than five letters, one extra point per letter beyond five.
Highest score wins.

Variation A

Dictate six words, each of which has anagrams. (There is a
goodly list above.) Allow three minutes for players to write
twistagrams for the dictated words. The one with most—but at
least one for every given word—wins.

Variation B

Make up sentences containing pairs of anagrams. Dictate the
sentences, saying BLANK instead of the anagrams. First to fill
in the right words wins. The sentence should be a clue to the
words left out. After two minutes, if there is little progress, tell
the number of letters. Thus:

1. He may have some — but it must lie —; he seems so medio-
cre.
2. A — must know how to take a proper —, to keep from swallowing water when a high wave comes.
            1. talent, latent   2. bather, breath

Variation C

For more skilled players, give each one a sheet on which you
have written a word that you know is an anagram, a different one

for each player. The player must write as many true anagrams as he can, for the word given him.

On a separate sheet, each player then writes sentences for the words he has on his first sheet BUT instead of writing the word, he puts a dash where a word on his list should come. At the top of the sheet he writes the number of letters in the word.

Papers are then exchanged; each player must fill in the blanks. First to get all correct wins. If, after three minutes, anyone is wholly baffled, he may be given the original word, from which he may then figure the anagrams.

Suppose the given word was CRATES. Anagrams are caters, reacts, recast. Sentences on the second sheet may run: I opened the — and took out the oranges. The man who — for parties took all he wanted. Tom, who — very quickly, — his ideas and helped make orangeade.

For a final anagrammateaser, try *scrambled monks*. Ask the players to make as many groups of words as they can, each group to use all the letters in the word monastery. Most in five minutes win. You'll be surprised how many there are. Here are some:

Tom yearns	not mar yes	yet no arms
nasty Rome	term so nay	tony mares
yon stream	my one star	my senator
stony mare	sty or mane	yeast morn
ay monster	O many rest	money arts
mare tansy	rest on may	stone Mary
tory means	no rye mats	Troy manes
Mary Stone	rye on mast	more nasty
no mastery	no Mars yet	many store
my treason	nest O Mary	O storm yen
mean story	tern O yams	try on seam

Anagames with Paraphernalia

So popular an activity as anagrams of course has attracted manufacturers of games. The first such game, called simply anagrams, provided small cards or chips (circles or squares), each with a letter on one side. You place these, blank side up, on the table. Each player in turn picks five, which he does not show. If with these letters he can form a word of at least four letters, he sets it in front of him, facing the other players, and picks one more letter from the table. So each in turn. Thereafter, each in turn picks up one letter; if he cannot make a word, he puts a letter from his hand on the table, face up.

Any player may, at his turn, take a word from another player if by adding one or more of his own letters (with or without letters from those face up on the table) he can form a new word. Plurals and other forms of the same word are not allowed, although a player may thus change his own word, to make it harder for others to take. When all the unseen letters have been picked from the table, the player with the most words wins.

A currently popular variation of anagrams is *scrabble,* for which one must buy a special board. Players may not appropriate an opponent's words. But each letter has a value on it, and a player may score extra points by having a letter cover a lucky spot on the board, marked as being worth double or triple the letter or the word. You must therefore try to place your word so that it will not give the others a chance to cover a lucky square.

No word can be placed next to one already on the board, unless it also uses the letter of the word that is down. Thus extra points can be scored by such combinations as:

```
                        O
T               M       E
HOTEL           E       N
E               N       O
N                       U
C                       G
E                       H
```

ALPHASTRIPS

You yourself can fashion a game of "strip-tcasc" anagrams. Take five narrow strips of cardboard, and print the letters of the alphabet (omitting Q) five down each strip.

Every player should be supplied with a set of alphastrips; give them the cardboard and let them make their own.

Players may then set the strips at any level they wish, but for one game cannot change this level. In five minutes, they make as many words as they can, using for any word only letters on the same level.

Score: five points for most words; one point for each three-letter word; three points for each four-letter word; ten points for each five-letter word. Highest score wins.

One player may set his strips at these levels:

```
              V
              W
     F  K     X
  A  G  L  P  Y
  B  H  M  R  Z
  C  I  N  S
  D  J  O  T
  E        U
```

Possible words of this pattern include: play, pay, lag, lay, gay, gapy, yap, gap, pal, gal, ply, sin, jot, dot

In other level-patterns, five letter possibilities include glary, hoary, whose, veils, rhyme

Variation

After players have learned to manipulate the alphastrips, they may set them at any level-pattern. *Now,* when they form a word, two letters must come from the same level; the remaining letters must come from the same column. In the level-pattern shown above, this variation gives, among other words:

folk, joust, coin, palm, glade, limns, gale, gape, bread, cads, chin, roust, huge, rude, crude, place, louts, suit, slap, strap, trips, sprint. Move the fourth strip up one, and there are rusty, grade, fight, hint, etc.

In this variation, score five points for five-letter words, and ten for six-letter words.

Many variations of word-forming games have been manufactured. Some work with dice, with a letter on each side.

One such game calls itself "Perquackey." Its 13 dice provide 78 letters; a sandglass provides three minutes, during which the one that has rolled the dice forms as many words as he can. Another, called "Spill and Spell," provides 15 dice, hence 90 letters.

Among the card games with letters, currently well known are "Spellbound" and "Bali." Both games have 54 cards, two "wild," that is, usable for any letter desired. In Bali, seven cards are laid face up on the table. In Spellbound, each player is dealt ten cards. In both games, words are made directly or by taking an opponent's letters or words. Once a word has been formed, the letters must be kept in that order. Rob, for example, may be captured as probe, throb, or robust, but cannot be converted into boar or brow.

It is clear that all such games are minor variations of anagrams. Their one added interest is the score; the letters are assigned values, and various types of extra points add to the possible total.

In spite of the vogue of one or another of these manufactured games, there is greater variety and consequent fun in the games you can fashion for yourself. Making them also increases your knowledge, and quickens your power of handling words.

7

The First and the Last and
Rhopes Between

The Acropolis is the City on the hill. *Acro–* indicates something sharp, a point, a peak. Gradually it was applied also to the point of departure, the beginning. An acrostic is a stanza in which the first letters of the successive lines spell a name. An acronym is a word formed from the first part of several words— Nabisco, radar. When you have company, you can work an

ACRODEAL

Each player writes his or her first name, one letter under the other. Then each writes a sentence, the first word of which begins with the first letter of the name, the second with the second, and so on. The group decides which sentence is most amusing. Thus there may be

S	how	M	any	S	earch
U	s	A		Y	ourself;
S	omething	R	ascal	B	eware
A	ltogether	G	ets	I	llusive
N	ew!	A	way;	L	icense!
		R	egard		
		E	thical		
		T	ransgressions.		

Variation A

Write the names as above; then papers are exchanged. Each player now tries to make his sentence fit the person whose name he has.

Variation B

Give all players the same name (full name) of a guest. See who writes the most amusing or appropriate sentence. Thus:

F	unicular	F	amiliar
R	ailways	R	emarks
A	re	A	nnoy
N	ever	N	eighbors
K	nown	K	eeping
T	o	T	heir
H	over	H	orsepower
O	ver	O	utside
L	ow	L	onely
T	errain.	T	averns.

Variation C

Same as above, *But* the letters of the name need not be the *first* letter of the words in the sentence. Thus:

w	H	en
th	E	y
we	N	t
	R	oaming
	Y	esterday
	T	hey
thoug	H	t
m	A	rvels
	W	aited.

Let us return to the initial consideration. To make some ACROTALES, each player puts his initials at the bottom of a sheet of paper. (Use three initials, making one up, if necessary, to make the game even.)

Exchange papers. Players write as the host dictates; then fold the paper to hide what they've written, and pass the paper to the player on the right. Again you tell them what to put down; they write, fold, and pass. Six times. And each time, what they write (three words) must begin with the letters (initials of the name) at the bottom.

You ask for: 1. three adjectives (fold under and pass) 2. three nouns 3. three verbs 4. three adverbs 5. three nouns 6. three nouns.

Thus, with my initials (J.T.S.), what is finally unfolded may read:

1. jolly	terrific	sloppy
2. jackal	toys	sheets
3. jangle	titillate	snuggle
4. jerkily	trustfully	suspiciously
5. jigsaw	temptation	simpleton
6. janitor	turkey	surrender

Players pass sheets again; no one is to have the sheet with his own initials. Allow a minute for players to open the sheets and plan. Then first player reads his first column, adding words to make sense. The first column above might be read—The jolly jackal began to jangle jerkily the jigsaw of the janitor.

Each player scores this for cleverness, rating from one to ten; the total score (sum of all the players' ratings) is placed at the top of the column. Second player reads his first column, which is scored the same way. Continue for all the papers; then read and score the second and the third column. Player whose initials have the highest total wins.

ACROCLUES

This is a game easy to prepare. Make a list of well-known persons. Next to each name write the initials, leaving a space between letters. Now write words beginning with these letters, and in some way applying to the person whose initials they are. Dictate the words to the players; first to get all the persons wins. You can multiply the fun if, amid the famous persons, you include the names of some of your guests. Here is a sampling of the procedure:

Acroclue	*Person*
1. He Could Amuse	8. Winston Churchill
2. Atomic Expert	7. Daniel Webster
3. Erratic American Poet	6. Harriet Beecher Stowe
4. Betrayed America	5. Christopher Columbus
5. Crossed Courageously	4. Benedict Arnold
6. Helped Bondsmen Suffering	3. Edgar Allan Poe
7. Debated Wonderfully	2. Albert Einstein
8. War Champion	1. Hans Christian Andersen

When you notice odd combinations of letters at the beginning of a word, jot them down. This will help add to your vocabulary, and to the fun you can have with your friends, with:

ACROGRAMS

Dictate some combinations of letters. The players are to write words beginning with those combinations. Player with most words in two minutes wins. Here are a few:

1. ghy	6. tmesis	4. utr	3. utmost
2. gey	5. alchemy, alcohol	5. alc	2. geyser
3. utm	Alcibiades	6. tme	1. ghyll
	4. utricle		

SENTENCE ME

Each player initials his sheet. Dictate five sentence-starts. Each player must complete the five sentences, as cleverly as he can. Collect, shuffle, and redistribute the papers; no one is to get his own. Each in turn reads sentence one. Player to the right tries to guess who wrote it. Score one for correct choice. When all versions of sentence one are read, group votes which is cleverest; Score two. Repeat this with all the sentences. Highest score wins. Here are some beginnings that have led to amusing ends:

If I had my way . . .
Women . . .
Psychoanalysts . . .
Under the stairway . . .
Just before dawn . . .
In my dream . . .
Just then the rain . . .
When the door opened . . .
On the desk . . .
He tilted her head . . .
If the sofa could speak . . .
When I was caught in the act . . .

Many good games can be made with prefixes, the rest of the word to be supplied. The simplest method is to give a prefix, and allow three minutes for players to write as many words as they can, "off the bat" as it were. So we can call this game *Acrobat.*

Or you can tell the prefix, then give clues from which the players must write the particular word beginning with that prefix which the clue indicates. Go to the bee, thou wordman; consider his ways, and bee wise. Ever so many words begin with be– and it is easy to make clues. Thus, What is the bee next you? Beside. Bee in the farmyard? Befoul (fowl). Bee on the top? Behead. Here are just a few more bees from the great hive:

betimes, behave, belief, bedeck, before, bestow, begun, bewail, below, behind, benign, belong, beware, berate, bedizen, because, behalf, bedraggle.

One of the earliest acrobat games I played came when my mother asked me to *Can* it! She did it with rhymes, which I find in her handwriting in a book dated 1905. Here they are:

1. Though this can is a can, you all will agree
   This can is termed thus because it holds tea.

2. This long narrow can holds so precious a stock
   That often you'll find it has more than one lock.
3. The most wick-ed can, though safe from police,
   If you search for its heart, you will find it in grease.
4. This is a can that delights you and me,
   It always is open and likewise is free.
5. Where breezes blow and surges roll
   With swelling form and manner proud,
   This can in triumph ruled the waves,
   The sailor's living—and his shroud.
6. Here's a can that, unrefined,
   Lives on others of its kind.
7. They say empty cans produce the most noise,
   But if properly filled this will startle the boys.
8. Most cans are hardly fit to eat;
   You needn't be a goat to like this treat.
9. The waltz or the glee or the bold martial strain,
   Each one his own favorite endorses;
   But for those that prefer oratorio style
   This can sweetest music discourses.
10. Now would you elect in a can to reside?
    Yet this can as a shelter is known far and wide.
11. A can of most sagacious mind,
    'Tis frugal, prudent, shrewd, you'll find.
12. That a horse should use cans seems indeed strange to say,
    Yet if pressed to have this one, he'd not utter a nay.
13. To put poems in cans very few are inclined,
    Yet cans of this sort in some poems you'll find.
14. In tubs and in bowls men have ventured from land,
    And in cans of this sort, though they often won't stand.
15. Here is a can that is yellow and round,
    It's good on the table but grows on the ground.

1. canister; 2. canal; 3. candle; 4. candor; 5. canvas; 6. cannibal; 7. cannon; 8. candy; 9. cantata; 10. canopy; 11. canny; 12. canter; 13. canto; 14. canoe; 15. cantelope.

When I was a boy, we played two games called CAT. In one, we hit a little stick with a bigger stick, and ran to base. In the other, we identified the pussy. For instance:

What cat is a:

1. waterfall
2. whip
3. deluge
4. list
5. two-hulled boat
6. howl
7. class
8. series of questions
9. burial place
10. great calamity
11. state of unconsciousness
12. spicy liquid

12. catsup
11. catalepsy
10. catastrophe
9. catacomb
8. catechism
7. category
6. caterwaul
5. catamaran
4. catalogue
3. cataclysm
2. cat-o'-nine-tails
1. cataract

Other cats on the premises are: catawba, catadupe, catafalque, catalysis, catadrome, cataplasm, cattle, catch, catasterism

Put the miss in the first place. Try not to be amiss, for then you miss. Dictate the questions; players write the answers; the one with the most right wins.

What miss:

1. may get one into trouble
2. believes all men are bad
3. acts wrongly
4. is tough luck
5. used to be lord one day a year
6. plays the wrong part
7. made an error
8. should be dodged by tourists
9. gives a false picture
10. is a villain
11. figures wrongly
12. makes a collection

12. miscellany
11. miscalculate
10. miscreant
9. misrepresent
8. misguide
7. mistake
6. miscast
5. misrule
4. misfortune
3. misbehave, misconduct
2. misanthrope
1. mischief

Other young ladies you can easily entice into the game are: miscible, misbegotten, misinterpret, misnomer, misspell, misbelief, misconceive, misjudge, mistrial, mistress, miscarry, misfit, mislead, mistral, mistify, mischance, misgovern, mislay, mister, misprint

There are also words that start with the gal. Make up your own clues, or ask the players to write down as many as they can think of in two minutes. They may have:

galahad, galley, gallop, gall, gallows, gallimaufry, gallant, gallery, Galileo, galvanize, galleon, galvanic, gallivant, Gallic, gala, galore, galligaskins, galaxy, gallet, galloon, galatea, gallipot, galimatias, gallinacean, galliwasp, galactagogue, galiot, galleas

Naturally, after the gal comes the man. Many a man awaits the wordwise player. Here are a few:

mantle, mantis, mansard, mandarin, manipulate, manganese, mangrove, manners, manicure, mandolin, mandate, manufacture, manor, manifold, manhandle, mantua, mankind, manacle, manager, manikin, manuscript, mansion, mange, Manhattan, manure—and manifestly there are many more.

Besides making up clues, or just asking for as many words as the players can think of, there is a third way of playing Acrobat.

Make sentences using words with the same prefix. Dictate these, BUT instead of giving the prefix words, say Blank. First player to fill the blanks properly wins. If they have trouble, tell them what the prefix is.

Here is a sample series of sentences:

Near the — to the town, outside which the army was —, the king sat —. He refused to — the plans of his general, protesting: "That will — our people!" His words were — in his councillors' memories. You can find his life in any —.

And you can find the words, in order, here: entrance, encamped, enthroned, endorse, enslave, engraved, encyclopedia.

Here are some other beginnings, which you can use in any of these three ways:

The industrious ant: antagonistic, antarctic, antenna, antonym . . .
The stubborn ass: assafoetida, assail, assassin, assume . . .
The fancy dive: divan, diverse, divorce, divulge, division . . .
The speedy car: caramel, cartridge, carnivorous, cartoon . . .

The questioning how: hound, housetop, howitzer, however, howbeit . . .

The funereal inter: interact, intercept; this could be interminable . . .

The pensive pen: pendulum, pending, penny, peninsula . . .

The unfortunately ill: illogical, Illinois, illstarred, illuminate . . .

The impish pan: pantheon, pandemonium, panacea, pancake . . .

The mischievous imp: imperfect, implausible, impecunious . . .

Flip the pages of the Index of *Roget's Thesaurus,* and you can find even trickier beginnings, with fewer words and therefore more challenge.

ACROGALLANT

While scientists may ponder the question which came first, the chicken or the egg—for does not this hold buried the secret of life?—there is no question that to a gentleman it is always the chicken: Ladies first. The first god was a goddess. This may not please the scientists or the Marxians, but it sets the conditions of this game.

Tell the players that every word begins with a girl's name.

1. Dictate the rest of the word. 2. Give a clue to the whole word. 3. Tell the number of letters in the girl's name. For instance (in these samples, dashes show the number of missing letters):

Word	*Clue*	*Name*
1. − − − − − cornered	crosswise	11. Fran
2. − − − mant	unyielding	10. Vera
3. − − − st	critter	9. Jo
4. − − − ard	small reptile	8. Bette
5. − − − ctive	resting	7. May
6. − − − ary	wages	6. Sal
7. − − − be	possibly	5. Ina
8. − − − − − r	more than good	4. Liz
9. − − in	put together	3. Bea
10. − − − − city	honesty	2. Ada
11. − − − − tic	frenzied	1. Kitty

While it is often wise to begin at the beginning—only epics begin *in medias res*—it is progressive not to stay there. The middle ways, the mediums, have their values. There need be nothing mean about the golden mean.

MIDDLEGRAMS

Try first with combinations of letters. Dictate an unusual combination. Allow players two minutes to write all the words they can think of, in which this combination occurs. Then dictate another combination. After five combinations, score five for each word, plus two points for each letter over six in a word. Highest score wins. Here are a few combinations, and a few words for each:

ln: kiln, fulness, dreadfulness, frightfulness
mp: prompt, imperialism, computations, extemporaneously, incomprehensibility
shw: freshwater, dishwater, fishways, dishwasher
cs: comics, discs, picnics, panics, frolicsome, cosmetics
tern: fraternize, patterns, externality, sauterne, eternity

The problem is not to find words, but to find long ones—quickly.
Tricky combinations of letters include:

ssp (misspell); rmb (alarmbell); ywh (anywhere, everywhere); ngr (ingredient, ingrown); epho (telephone); dpec (woodpecker); also bfu, ssf, wkw, nten, roca, rmom, rch

What word has three double letters in succession? repeekkoob (Turn it around.)

Variation A

Prepare sentences in advance, using in them words that contain a combination of letters you choose. Dictate the sentences, *But* instead of the words with the combination, say Blank. Tell how many letters are in the combination.

After two minutes, all players that have found the combination score five points. Tell the combination. After three more minutes, score two for every word correctly inserted.

You can make sentences easily, with any combination. Here is a series, with p.o.s.

Despite his —, John would not — the trip, feeling that would be an — on the rest. He — would not — his difficulties on them. "I —," he said, "that by five — the — will close, but we can telegraph ahead. Perhaps a — exhumation, for a — examination, would show me to be —; then I may quietly —."

Try solving this yourself, before you try it on your friends.

The words, in order, are: indisposition, postpone, imposition, positively, impose, suppose, P.M. (post meridian), postoffice, posthumous, postmortem, non compos mentis, decompose.

Variation B

Tell the players what the combination of letters is. Then dictate the clues; players are to write the words. First finished wins. Here is a sample set with the same combination:

Clue	*Word*
1. put across	10. adipose
2. rest	9. post
3. behind	8. posture
4. after Noah	7. positive
5. own	6. composition
6. something put together	5. possess
7. mistaken at the top of one's voice	4. postdiluvial
8. position in life	3. posterior
9. mail	2. repose
10. too much	1. transpose

MIDDLEPUT

Sometimes the middle of a word is another word. Tell the players:

1. the first and the last letter.
2. the number of letters in between. (In the samples, three).

1. c – – – n; 2. c – – – y; 3. b – – – l; 4. h – – – t;
5. b – – – h

Allow two minutes. Then give clues, double. Here are clues (and the answers) for the five given on the previous page.

Tuck in	*and get*	*Word to insert*
1. what's around you	a pile of stones	5. rot
2. a conjunction	a treat	4. ear
3. Lincoln	confusion	3. abe
4. an organ	an organ	2. and
5. nonsense	soup	1. air

Other words with lesser words within their bords to bind them include: scape, spare, spine, trunk, speak, wrath, thumb, groves, haughty, severe, bleak, brand, brought, party, chasm, daily, dilly, dally, facet, fever, glade, stark, pride, boner, brandy, frighten, caret, cloth, dairy, effaced, flamed, honey, stare, whist, bored, brawl, cater, clean, dreary, fabled, Galen, valet, sleet, scramble (cram, ram). Plurals and verb forms add to the number: vends, bends, blows, brats, crusts, bails, bilks, bodes, treads, chicks, basks, blots, boils, bluffs, tramples (ramp, ample). This can go on: praised, grounds, emerged, weights, sampler, pirates, maligns, slattern, magenta, proverb, narrows, seventh, slumbery, tracery, aspired, cleans, tramps, thorns, beasts, centers, salient, routs, against, plunger, rends, oration, turns, chasten, lottery, charts, triter, cleanse, sloth

Many a word, losing its first letter, remains a word. Dictate clues in pairs, one for the full word, one for the new word, in the game DROP ONE.

In the example given, tell the players that they can check, for the dropped letters, properly arranged, spell a word.

Clue	*becomes* (dropped letter clue)	*Word*
1. thrown violently	air chamber	9. tease
2. on high	top storey	8. about
3. a tree	coy	7. yours
4. occurrence	a passage-way	6. taunt

Clue	*becomes* (dropped letter clue)	*Word*
5. delete	destroy	5. erase
6. mock	relative	4. event
7. your property	ours	3. larch
8. preposition	contest	2. aloft
9. annoy	comfort	1. flung

Dropped letters clue: A French aristocrat who helped the American Revolution (Turn around etteyafaL)

Perhaps you can make the dropped letters spell something related to one of your guests. Here are some more words the first letters of which can be dropped:

gloom, broad, stale, price, praise, gloam, brow, close, plain, cleave, bright, crack, player, place, clever, revoke, craven, then, swarm, flaw, trite, slate, crock, stile, shovel, flight, snag, again, emission, slit, shaven, stray, draw, fright, estate

Some words can be decapitated more than once. Thus:

meat, eat, at; chit, hit, it; still, till, ill; shave, have, ave; blowing, lowing, owing, wing; clover, lover, over; spark, park, ark; wheat, heat, eat, at; prelate, relate, elate, late, ate

Variation A

Ask players to write as many words as they can think of, that can drop the first letter and be another word. Allow five minutes.

Score: for each 2-word series, 2 points. For 3-word series, 5 points. For 4-word series, 10 points; 5-word series, 15 points. Highest score wins.

Variation B

Limit the players to words beginning with t. Here are a few such teasers. Allow three minutes; the one with most words wins.

tease, that, tape, thick, true, turn, then, tart, this, twaddle, those, tone, twit, trusty, trappings, tale, taunt, train, terror, trash, trifle, twit, transom, trend, tend, thug, thence, tweed, tracer

Variation C

TEE-OFF. This has no relation to golf. After Variation B, from the list they have made, players should select six words, and make up sentences for them. On a new sheet of paper, each player should write his sentences, using both words of the pair (T on and T off), *But* where the words should come he writes a dash. Exchange papers; allow five minutes for players to set in the right words. For each pair, two points; highest score wins. Here are some possible sentences:

1. He was so rich he could almost — the whole —.
2. His having that Russian — almost got him into —.
3. As he died —, his — was divided as he wished.
4. I'd hate to — with that guy unless I knew his —.
5. We hated to go out of the warm — into the chill —.
6. Not many students are — to construct a logarithm —.
6. t able; 5. t rain; 4. t angle; 3. t estate; 2. t rouble; 1. t own

LETTER OUT

This is a simpler game. It can be played only once with the same group, because it has a catch in it, and you go on playing until someone in the group discerns the trick.

The leader says: "I want your help. I don't like peas. What vegetable can I eat?" He asks each player in turn. Player questioned names a vegetable, and the leader says "Thank you!" or "Sorry!" What he does not like are p's; for any vegetable with the letter *p* he says "Sorry!"

The same game can be played with the start: "I don't like tea. What would you suggest that I drink?" And he is Sorry for all drinks (like martinis or tomato juice) that contain the letter *t*.

SECOND TAKE

Many words can become other words by the removal of their second letter. Dictate, for several such—clue for the whole word, and clue for the new word when the second letter is removed. First to get all the words wins. Here are a few:

Clue (whole)	Clue (minus second letter)	Word (whole)
1. simple	hurt	8. shave
2. husky bee	completed	7. show
3. not fresh	special offering	6. spill
4. small shovel	dryer	5. gloat
5. stare trium- phantly	butter	4. trowel
6. upset	window-ledge	3. stale
7. display	before you reap	2. drone
8. cut hair	economize	1. plain

Variation

Ask players to list as many such words as they can find in three minutes. Here are a few. Clues, if you want to play that way, are easy to fashion.

bland, thin, print, crape, drive, blank, store, place, crap, bleak, crane, friend, clamp, clove, slender

PUT AND TAKE

Dictate the pairs of words. Players are, in each pair, to take one letter out of the first word and give it to the second word—so that the two words can then be rearranged to form two other words. The new pair will be related in meaning. Thus: rung and file. Transfer the r; you can make gun and rifle.

Dictated pair	Related pair
1. bread and pot	9. boat and ship
2. whoms and pleas	8. pat and stroke
3. eclat and more	7. land and ground
4. rated B and rebut	6. moo and bleat
5. nines and cates	5. sine and secant
6. loom and beat	4. bread and butter
7. gland and round	3. late and comer
8. part and stoke	2. show and sample
9. boast and hip	1. bard and poet

Variation

Instead of giving the first pair, give clues to them. Players must then discover the first pair, and after that must find the letter to remove and discover the second, related pair of words. Here are:

Clues	*First pair*
1. up the ladder and keep for the record	9. bleat and fail
2. stoppers and style	8. fleet and sate
3. makes hot and maize	7. kail and sic
4. give vent and default	6. stir and miser
5. small wagon and maximum humidity	5. cart and rain
6. agitate and skinflint	4. wreak and fail
7. cole and so it goes	3. heats and corn
8. swift and glut	2. corks and tone
9. calf's cry and not make the grade	1. rung and file

I'll leave you to find the second, related pairs, by transferring the underlined letters.

MEANDER

The word meander comes from a river in Turkey, and flying over it not long ago, I saw that we have employed the term aptly. Let's try it with words.

Each player should write a three-letter word. He should then drop the first letter and add one letter at the end, so as to form a new word. Player with the longest Meandering in three minutes wins. Thus:

was-asp-spa-pan-any-N.Y.C.
the-her-era-raw-awe-wet-eta-tar-are-red
aid-Ida-dad-ado-don-one-new-ewe-wen-end
the-her-era-rat-ate-ten-end
cab-Abe-Ben-Ena-nag-age-get-eta-tar-are-rev-eve
key-eye-yea-eat-ate-tea-eat-ate-tea-ear-are-ret-eta-tab-Abe-Ben-end

The last line above shows the reason for another Rule in this game—no word is to be repeated in any single flow.

Variation

Try this with four letter words. Meander as before, except: instead of dropping at start and adding at end, you form a new word by changing any one letter, each time. Thus:

beat-boat-coat-cost-lost-lose-dose-dost-dust-bust-best-rest-rust-lust-lost-most-must-mist-fist-gist-list-lint-line . . .

At this point (as at other points) you can take either of two meanderings:

fine-tine-tiny-tony . . .

or   lane-fane-pane-pale-pall-tall-tail-sail-mail-rail-bail-ball-call-hall-halt . . . Let's call a halt!

Longest meander in three minutes wins.

Variation, CROW FLIGHT

You could also call this *Bee Line,* save that the bees do a dance to let their hivemates know where they've found good sucking-ground.

Give the players two words of the same number of letters, and some tie of sense. They are to travel from one to the other by making new words changing one letter at a time. The one that makes the journey in the shortest number of words wins. Thus:

Words	*Journey (words between)*
ship—sail	skip-skid-said
sing—talk	sang-sank-tank
hand—foot	hard-lard-lord-ford-fort (There's a shorter journey for this: band-bond-fond-food)
sin—woe	son-won (How quick the sequence if not consequence!)
hate—love	have-lave (How near and yet how far!)
black—white	slack-stack-stalk-stale-shale-whale-while

BURIED WORDS

Sometimes a word lies hidden in successive letters within another word, or perhaps the last letters of one word and the first
letters of another together form a separate word. It is not hard,
indeed, to arrange some buried words yourself. Let's start with
animals.

Take a donkey. Break the word; and think of words that end
with the first part: abandon, Don, London, celadon, mastodon,
myrmidon. Then words that begin with the second part: key,
keyed up, Key West, keynote, keystone. Then make a sentence,
for instance: An army should never abandon key situations.

Or try mouse. The combination *ou* is good to break, because
separating the sound may fool some players. Thus you may
write: Will a dynamo use more power than it generates?

Caution: If you have to use an unusual word to fit in your buried
word, put another unusual word somewhere else in the sentence.
One unusual word will attract attention; two will divide it.

Perhaps you can bury a name of a person expected at your
party.

Here is an aviary for an ornithologist. But he'll have to hunt
for his birds. John Kieran once told me he had spotted 107 varieties flying along Riverdale. See how many your friends can spy
on the wing, in this passage:

The big stern wheel of the river steamer lingers, and at last
begins to revolve; a gleam of light from the paddle, and overhead
a wreath of smoke belched from the ravenous maw of the
furnace, and the deferred starting is forgotten. Again the waiting
crowd, swallowing its late bitterness and smarting, resumes its
cheerful march and chatter, voices hum merrily, and the gang-
ways fill with rushing feet. A shout now rends the air as two
meagre, belated Swedish-Americans are seen running toward
the boat, the taller one traversing with awkward strides the

tarpaulin nets and traps of hard-working fishermen without asking let or hindrance; the other one, a small, ardent fellow, puffing away behind, runs with rasher haste down a gully as if in cheering view of lost riches. Meanwhile the boat is stealing away from the wharf and the gang-plank is lifting. An Irishman with matches and pipe rammed into his pocket, his blouse lappet released from his pantaloons, with a face like a saint and a nose like a parsnip, edges from the walnut hatchway to the rail and howls:

"Did I 'ver see the loikes? Tre-le-le-a-a-a-la! Bejaybers I bet on long Racklebones, and a booby prize for the butterball."

Then the tall Swede, being swifter afoot, jumps upon the departing gangway, and turning calls to his companion who stands quailing on the edge of the wharf:

"Yump, Yohn, Yump! I tenk you can mek it..en..two.. yumps."

Hidden in the foliage of words are the following birds, in order: tern, merlin, eagle, dove, daw, raven, red start, crow, swallow, bittern, martin, fulmar, chat, hummer, thrush, wren, grebe, hawk, linnet, kingfisher, heron, mallard, puffin, thrasher, gull, finch, ostrich, teal, sandpiper, ousel, petrel, loon, snipe, nuthatch, rail, owl, diver, kestrel, jay, grackle, boob, butterball, hen, swift, quail, kite.

MARSUPIALS

The kangaroo word, or marsupial, holds a special sort of buried word. The big word has a little word inside, the letters in the right order though not necessarily adjacent; *And* the little word is a synonym of the big one.

Give an example, and give the players three minutes to write all the marsupials they can think of. There will be few.

Variation

Spell a few marsupials, which the players write down, *But* say Blank instead of giving the letters that are the little word. First to fill the blanks wins. Here are a few marsupials. Try them yourself.

1. pro – ec – t –	Tuck in:	13. e.v.i.n.c.e
2. pe – – – eter		12. b.l.o.o.m
3. – eg – – at –		11. i.d.l.e
4. tran – gress – o –		10. m.a.t.e.s
5. s – r – – gle		9. r.e.s.t
6. – – scu – in –		8. e.r.r
7. ex – – ts		7. i.s
8. ab – – – ate		6. m.a.l.e
9. – – – pi – e		5. t.u.g
10. – – – ch – –		4. s.i.n
11. – n – o – – nt		3. r.u.l.e
12. – – – ss – –		2. r.i.m
13. – – – de – – –		1. s.u.e

TWIN ENDS

Some words have the same letters at both ends. Tell this to the players, with an example (diabetic's delight—insulin). Then dictate the center letters, telling how many you've omitted fore and aft. Players are to find the missing twins. If they make little progress, give them clues. For instance:

Word	Clue	Twin Ends
1. – – it – –	prepared for print	6. sh
2. – – erne – –	most severe	5. es
3. – – sta – –	with a will	4. de
4. – – ri – –	mock	3. te
5. – – senc – –	spirits	2. st
6. – – ellfi – –	molluscs	1. ed

You can find many twin-end words yourself, then easily make clues for them. Here is a hunting hint.

Take a common ending, such as *er, est, ing.* In the Index to *Roget's Thesaurus,* look up the words beginning with those letters, and see how many can be fitted with the same ending. Here are some:

es: (This permits nouns plural, and verbs singular) – – ca-pad – –; – – pi – –; – – tuari – –; – – cap – –; – – tablish – –; – – timat – –

le: (the ones with three dashes are ble) – – – acha – – –;
– – – eda – – –; – – – ssa – – –; – – adab – –; – – afab – –;
– – gislatab – –

(Note: Manifestly the final *b* in most of these would betray the word, if you put several together in a game. The same is true of other forms. In a game, do not dictate many of the same twins together.)

ent: – – anglem – – –; – – – ertainm – – –; – – – hralm – – –;
– – – hronem – – –; – – – rapm – – –; – – – rainm – – –
te: – – amma – –; – – mpera – –; – – nua – –; – – rmina – –;
– – rtia – –; – – ssela – –
th: – – erewi – –; – – inne – –; – – ickene – –; – – inke – –;
– – eopa – –
or: – – at – –; – – iginat – –
res: – – – pi – – –; – – – to – – –
ph: – – onogra – –; – – otogra – –

If these look easy, it may be because the twin is before you. Look at these:

1. – – – ather – – –; – – – erminat – – –; – – – enerat – – –;
– – – raft – – –
2. – – adac – –; – – artac – –
3. – – eepi – –; – – rewi – –
4. – – – – man – – – –
5. – – tinomi – –
6. – – g – –; – – uc – –; – – ucat – –; – – ifi – –; – – ulcorat – –
7. – – range – –; – – onie – –; – – ale – –; – – eale – –; – – eep-
e – –; – – ronge – –; – – ate – –; – – iffe – –; – – ickie – –;
– – raighte – –

Here are the twins I've just numbered: 1. ing 2. he 3. sh
4. ship 5. an 6. ed 7. st The final *e* may have helped you here. This is the largest source of twin-ends, because it forms the superlative, as in sturdiest, and also the "whither thou goest" form of the verb, as when thou stowest away a full meal. Bon appetit!

THE PALINDROME

Some words are not only twins, but identical twins—they are the same spelled front to back and back to front. We call such a word a palindrome, from the Greek term for runaround. Here are some words and even sentences that read the same from left to right as from right to left:

bob; gag; pip; minim; civic; refer; level; deified; Malayalam. Every word of the jealous mother's question: Did Dad eye Ada? And the whole rueful reflection of the wounded soldier: Snug & raw was I ere I saw war & guns. The alarmclock rings on Election Day: Rise to vote, Sir! Then there's the frightened mouse that squealed: Was it a cat I saw?

Scramble a palindrome. Tell the players how many words are in the sentence. While they are figuring it out, you'll have time to refill the ice-cube container. For instance:
eeiioorrssttv four words.

Helpful hint. The odd letter must of course be midway. On each side of it, the same letters must be placed. In this sample, then, set V in the middle; on each side you must place E I O R S T. It should then be easy to figure out that this is what the alarm clock rang on Election Day.

LEARNING THE RHOPES

Ancient peoples, even after the stone-age men of our comics, were familiar with the club. (The one for physical, not verbal, argument) The Greeks called it rhopalon. From the shape of the club, lines of verse in which each word has a letter more, or a syllable more, than the word before it are called rhopalic. In rhopalic game words, each uses every letter of the word before, plus one. Thus:

a, at, tan, rant, train, rating, darting, drafting
a, an, ran, rain, train, strain, rainest, trainers, restrains, transpires
I, if, fit, fist, first, strife, trifles, stiflers, lifteress
I, is, sit, site, deist, stride, redints, strident
I, in, pin, pint, print, sprint, pinster (a bowler), spinster, splinters, turnipless
O, on, ton, tone, stone, honest, thrones, shortens

a, Ra, era, sear, erase, sealer, reveals
A, ah, hat, heat, hates, hearts, threads, thrashed
I, if, fir, rife, fired, rifted, trifled, filtered
a, at, ate, rate, crate, create, reacted, decorate, decorated
       : react, tracer, creator, creators
       : seat, yeast
       : beat, bathe, bather, halbert, halberts
       : teal, lathe, lather, halters
       : late, later, relate, reslate, alteress

Here's one that rhopes along without shifting the letters: a, at, ate, elate, relate, prelate, prelates

And here are a few that just tuck letters on at the end:
car, care, cares, caress
be, bee, beer, beery
cap, cape, caper, capers

Just as a sample from the ancients, here is a syllabic rhope probably devised by a pious monk trying to keep awake during the service—Spes deus aeternae stationis conciliator (God the befriender is your hope of an eternal place).

RHOPEM

Explain rhopes to the players. Allow them three minutes to build up a rhope series. One with the longest wins.

Variation

Make clues for a rhope series. Dictate the clues. First to get the words wins. For instance:

1. Start with an article	8. pediatry
2. You're there	7. partied
3. Food was consumed before the show	6. pirate
4. value it	5. irate
5. angry	4. rate
6. this fellow's a water-rat	3. ate (8 P.M.)
7. given a celebration	2. at
8. taking care of the children	1. a

RHOPE ALONG

Players write a sentence, the first word having one syllable, the second two syllables, and so on—as long as they can make it. The last word may again be of one syllable. The group decides which is cleverest. Read them a sample; here are two:

Glut, giddy gorebellied gormandizer, guzzleduzzeling gastronomically!

Men invite damosels attractively ornamentalized, investigatingly, semisolicitously, lewd.

If you are in the company of word-fanciers, you can make an extra rule: Every word must begin with the same letter—as in the first example above.

Variation

For a trickier Rhope game, give each player a sheet of paper and a number. Each player writes a one-syllable word, and his number under it. Papers are passed to the right; now each writes a two-syllable word and puts his number under it. The two words must make sense or valid nonsense. Pass papers again for three-syllable words, and again for four.

Continue. *But,* if the player cannot think of an appropriate five-syllable word, he may write a word of one syllable. At any time after four, if a player is stuck, he may use a one-syllable word, BUT only once on any one sheet. After the one-syllable word, start building again. If a player cannot think of a word of the right number of syllables, he must pass the sheet on without writing a word or his number. Continue passing, for twelve words. Then sheets are read. Each player scores one point for every syllable in every appropriate word his number is under, on any sheet. If the group thinks a word does not fit, two points off. Highest score wins. Here is such a rhopalic sentence:

An army officer admonishing insubordinate fools started laughingly disregarding inconsequential regulationary rules.

As in this example, you may add a rule that the middle and the end monosyllables rhyme.

Here is a rhopalic passage you can dictate, with blanks to be filled in:

– don't like – –, said the man in the black – – –. It is true that the – – – – is impressive, but when we – – – – – a man, we – – – – – – a – – – – – – – identity. There will be a – – – – – – – – against – – – – – – – – – when the – – – – – – – – – of this is recognized.

You should not have much trouble with the first three in this rhope. The very last one flashed into my mind when I tried it; this speeded up the process of filling the blanks, with the words: I, it, tie, rite, inter, retain, certain, reaction, cremation, importance.

ANARHOPE

Give the players a word (any word from the list of rhopes above will serve); allow three minutes for them to reduce it to a word of one letter, by lowering it through other words, one letter less each time. This is, of course, the reverse of the Rhoping process. Thus:

flotsam, floats, float, foal, oaf, of, O
chosen, hosen, hone, hoe, ho, O
          : cones, cone, one, on, O
sprouted, sported, poster, trope, port, tor, or, O
spaniels, spaniel, panels, plane, pane, nap, an, a
                    : plan, pan, an, a
cheaters, teaches, cheats, teach, heat, ate, at, a
drowned, wonder, drown, down, own (don), on, O

A special form of Anarhope, which we may call Decapitation, cuts down the series by always removing the first letter. Thus: scrape, crape, rape, ape. And there was the teacher in Edinburgh who put a note on his door: "Professor Dunbar will not meet his classes today." Passing by shortly after, the professor noticed that some wag had rubbed off the first letter of the word classes. Thereupon the professor rubbed off the second letter. We must assess our actions, lest we lose that final s.

Most things are sortable into threes. A circle has a center, radius, and circumference. We are born, we marry, and we die. A plot, says Aristotle, has a beginning, a middle, and an end. We have now, with words, come to the end.

ENDERS

Let him that is without sin cast the first stone. How about the last stone?

Players have three minutes to write all the words they can think of, ending with -stone. Such as:

brimstone, clingstone, cornerstone, curbstone, whetstone, cobblestone, flagstone, foundation-stone, grindstone, soapstone, touchstone, hailstone, headstone, hearthstone, holystone, moonstone, Yellowstone, keystone, limestone, lodestone, milestone, millstone

Variation

Tell the ending. Dictate clues. Players are to write (or guess aloud) the word. Here, from my mother's notebook, are some rhymed frozen endings:

Guess the name of the ice that are frightened by cats,
The ice that tastes good in a cake.
The ice that you pay for the goods that you buy,
The ice that you don't like to take.
The ice, thick or thin, that is cut from a loaf,
The ice that's a brief space of time;
The ice that is never repeated but once,
The ice that grows in a warm clime.
The ice that's an emblem and also a scheme,
The ice that are shaken and thrown;
The ice that's exact, that is fine and refined,
The ice that is best left alone.

Here, in order, are the ices; mice, spice, price, advice, slice, trice, twice, rice, device, dice, nice, vice

Here are some after dinner clues, in prose.

1. never ate alone	14. terminate
2. always ate with his superiors	13. exaggerate
3. ate very daintily	12. masticate
4. ate in lusty vein	11. procrastinate
5. ate like another	10. candidate
6. ate while rising	9. delegate
7. ate from bad to worse	8. fascinate
8. ate so as to cast a spell	7. deteriorate
9. ate for someone else	6. elevate
10. ate with promises	5. imitate
11. never ate today what he could eat tomorrow	4. invigorate
	3. delicate
12. ate thoroughly	2. subordinate
13. overate	1. associate
14. was always last to eat (so we pause)	

If it's too easy to see how persons ate, you can step the game one letter up by making a date with capricious Kate. Have players write all the words they can think of, ending -date or -cate; or else make up clues for some of these words, and dictate the clues.

Thus:
What's the date that makes things clear? elucidate
Who's the Kate that clears you? vindicate
More: inundate, postdate, invalidate, antedate, dilapidate, sedate, liquidate, consolidate, intimidate, predate, prevaricate, duplicate, rusticate, lubricate, advocate, domesticate, suffocate, confiscate, excommunicate, intoxicate, implicate

Other endings that can be used for such games include:

dental: accidental, transcendental, coincidental, occidental . . .
mental: governmental, nutrimental, regimental, temperamental . . .
under: asunder, blunder, plunder, refunder, rotunder, thunder . . .

air: affair, declare, anywhere, ensnare, impair, dare, prayer . . .
        (Note that either sound or spelling counts)
each: beach, beech, overreach, preach, screech, beseech,
peach . . .
osity: vious; rious; ality; ivity, ility; and many more. Let's try
a sting in the tail: roasting, resting, encrusting, molesting. . . .

If you are tired of walking, try the L. You can make this very
tricky. Dictate the clues. Tell players the clues are for pairs of
words; each word becomes another if you add fifty at the end.
After they have struggled for a while, tell them that it is the
Roman fifty (L) which they should add. All the words change
into other words by adding *l* or *el*.

Clue	*Word*
Add 50 to:	
1. a push and get a spade	12. bush el
2. a drink and get a water-fowl	11. cow l
3. a charge and get sensitive	10. bow l
4. a friend and get a dark cloud	9. sea l
5. an open mouth and get beat up	8. pane l
6. a girl and get a record	7. grave l
7. serious and get paving	6. anna l
8. a glass and get a jury	5. maw l
9. a body of water and get one of	
its denizens	4. pal l
10. a curtsey and get a dish	3. fee l
11. an animal and get a hood	2. tea l
12. a plant and get a measure	1. shove l

You can give yourself L with many words to make new words,
and clues should come easy. Here are just a few more words, in
case you are lazy today:

anima l, hove l, trow el, pea l, came l, tow el, shaw l, draw l
So let's not fight a due l, but have a peaceful end.

8

Squares to Vary Cross Words

Words and figures have always gone together. The better the figure, the fewer the words.

Before words became holy* and thus gained sanctuary, children used to play a game called:

HANGMAN

Hangman is a game that two can play.

One player puts dashes on a sheet of paper, each dash representing one letter of a word he has in mind. The other player guesses a letter. If that letter is in the word, first player writes it over the dash where it belongs. If not, he draws a gallows-pole on the paper. For each wrong guess he draws another stage of the hanging: crossbeam, then a rope, then a circle for the doomed man's head, then a line for the body, a line for each arm and leg—feet and buttons if necessary—until the other player has guessed the right word.

Then the second player puts down dashes, and the first has to guess. Each tries to escape hanging by a bigger margin. The game continues until the players run out of words, time, or patience. *Note:* since the first guesses will naturally be vowels

* Cross words, of course.

(starting with the most common, *e,*) good words to select are those with unexpected combinations, such as S P R U N G or L A R Y N X. An odd word like P Y X might seem hard, but once the Y is set in the middle, the whole word is likely to flash into the mind . . . now go and be hanged!

SQUARES

The ubiquitous crossword puzzle had many antecedents, growing from the simple anagram. One of the earliest patterns was the square. The following square was found, scratched in ancient Latin, on a Roman wall in England.

A word square is a combination of letters that read the same across and down—row one and column one are the same word; row two and column two, and so on.

The Latin example above is more complicated, because it is also a palindrome—the same working from either end, starting at top or bottom, running left or right. The Latin words mean— Arepo the sower holds the wheels to the work.

Dictate clues for the words in the square. (Each word will of course have as many letters as there are words in the square.) Here are a few to give:

Clues		*Words*					
A. 1. a narrow road	E.	P	A	S	T	O	R
2. a surface		A	T	T	I	R	E
3. not far		S	T	U	P	I	D
4. sense organs		T	I	P	T	O	E
		O	R	I	O	L	E
		R	E	D	E	E	M

Clues		*Words*

B. 1. halt   D. W A S T E
   2. dry   A C T O R
   3. not yours   S T O N E
   4. paradise   T O N I C
                       E R E C T

C. 1. vital organ
   2. weird
   3. got up   C. H E A R T
   4. elevated   E E R I E
   5. adolescent years   A R O S E
                       R I S E N
D. 1. squander   T E E N S
   2. player
   3. small rock
   4. pick-me-up   B. L A M E
   5. upright   A R I D
                       M I N E
E. 1. shepherd   E D E N
   2. dress
   3. dumb
   4. walking quietly   A. L A N E
   5. a bird   A R E A
   6. ransom   N E A R
                       E A R S

SCRAMBLED SQUARES

Here the cue is an anagram (scrambled word). The letters must be rearranged to form the right word. Then the words must be arranged to form a square.

Anagram	*Word (Number shows correct order)*
A. nead	B. 5. harps
satk	4. stamp
dens	1. smash
etme	2. Malta
	3. altar
B. rahsp	
tamsp	C. 5. treat
hamss	4. Celia
tlmaa	1. tract
tlraa	3. apple
	2. riper

	Anagram		*Word (Number shows correct order)*
C.	ertta	A. 2.	Edna
	eclai	4.	task
	rctat	3.	ends
	ppela	1.	meet
	prier		

Here are some squares for you to scramble, or make clues for— or just to look at and try to create more:

```
E A T     B U S     D I M     B L O W     H O M E
A R E     U S E     I R E     L A V A     O V E N
T E A     S E T     M E T     O V A L     M E N D
                              W A L K     E N D S
W O M E N     H E A R T
O L I V E     E N T E R
M I N E S     A T O N E
E V E R T     R E N T S
N E S T S     T R E S S
```

DOUBLE SQUARES have words of four letters, except the middle word. This has seven letters, tying the squares together.

```
      F A I R               P O R E
      A C R E               O V A L
      I R O N               R A R E
      R E N T I N G         E L E C T E D
          I D E A               T E A R
          N E L L               E A S E
          G A L E               D R E W

      S T I R               H O P E
      T I D E               O M E N
      I D E A               P E T S
      R E A D E R S         E N S U R E S
          E V I L               R E A P
          R I D E               E A S E
          S L E D               S P E D
```

Here is one Double Square, scrambled:

Scrambles	Words	Order
1. emta	7. pool	3
2. ploo	6. neat	5
3. sapl	5. step	7
4. tinslps	4. splints	4
5. ptse	3. Alps	1
6. tane	2. loop	2
7. olop	1. tame	6

This is a tricky one, as several of the scrambles can make more than one word. The players must test to see which fits the square. Thus he must choose among: laps, slap, pals, Alps; step, pets, pest; meat, mate, tame; polo, pool, loop.

And here is one Double Square to be guessed through clues:

Clues	Words	Order
1. space	7. near	3
2. the first garden	6. rang	1
3. White Christmas	5. Nero	6
4. planted places	4. gardens	4
5. Roman Emperor	3. snow	7
6. sounded a bell	2. Eden	5
7. not far	1. area	2

DIAMOND WORDS

Words can also be shaped like a girl's best friend. Rows will always have odd numbers of letters. You can ignore the top and bottom single letters; once you have the center word, you fill these in. Here is a simple diamond:

```
                      P
Clues: juice of the olive     O I L
       evergreens         P I N E S
       meadow                L E A
                              S
```

Here are a few more. Give the clues; allow five minutes for each diamond. *Clues:*

A. a garden tool   B. top   C. precious stone
   substantives   papal crown   danger
   extremity   gem   high officer
                             haughty   singer by night
                             conjunction   great marvel
                                             long spoon
                                             sheltered side

```
                S                         D
              G E M                     T I P
            P E R I L                 T I A R A
          G E N E R A L       B.  D I A M O N D
     C. S E R E N A D E R             P R O U D
          M I R A C L E               A N D
            L A D L E                 D
              L E E
                R
```

```
                  N
                H O E
         A.  N O U N S
                E N D
                  S
```

Here, for veterans, is a Maltese Cross made of four diamonds joined in the center. One letter of the longest word in each cross ties it to the center. These center words can be read either in to the center or out from it. The clues are:

Top Diamond: queen of the fairies; married lady; wicked
Right Diamond: possessed; makes the sea; lair
Bottom Diamond: strike; narrow; article
Left Diamond: hard-shelled fruit; Turkish flower; metal
Center Cross (reading out, clockwise starting at top): male
     sheep; not cooked; rodent; sharp blow

Center Cross (reading in, clockwise starting at top): spoil; open conflict; thick liquid; equal

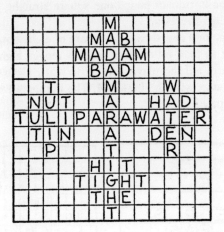

LOTTO WORDS

This should provide a lot o' words. Give players squared paper; there should be 5 rows of 5 boxes, each box large enough to hold a letter.

First player calls a letter; every player puts it into any box he wishes. Next player calls a letter. The object is to place the letters into boxes so that words can be spelled, up, down, right, left, or diagonally. Continue until all 25 boxes are filled.

There may be more than one word in a line. One letter may count in as many words as it fits. Thus METOO scores me, met, too. Pants (trousers) also scores pa, pan, pant (breathe), an, ants (not both ant and ants).

Score: two-letter word, two points; three-letter word, five points; four-letter word, ten points; five-letter word, 15 points. Highest score wins.

For a more difficult game, make six boxes in six rows. Then only words of three or more letters count.

KNIGHTLY WORDS

As heralds and chessplayers know, the knight is a great leaper. In chess, the horseman jumps one square straight, then one diagonal, in any direction.

Set letters on a chessboard (a square of eight boxes in each of eight rows) so that, following a knight's moves, they spell a sentence. Always tell the players where to start. Here is a Knightly Sentence—start with the Letter M. The numbered squares show the proper path.

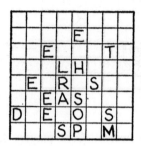 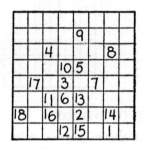

It is easy to make Knightly Words. Take any proverb, or make up your own sentence, making sure it has no more than 64 letters. Below are five patterns of knight moves that cover every square on the board.

Follow the numbers on Square A, B, C, D, or E, putting the letters of your words in numerical order. In Squares C and D, the step from 64 to one is also a knight's move; so you can begin your path anywhere you want.

Always tell the players where to start.

Square E also leads from 64 to one. But it will also interest numerologists, for it is a magic square—every column and every row adds to 260.

Square F is also a magic square—BUT this makes not the knight's moves but the king's moves: one space at a time, in any direction. This also can give players a trail to hunt.

A

34	49	22	11	36	39	24	1
21	10	35	50	23	12	37	40
48	33	62	57	38	25	2	13
9	20	51	54	63	60	41	26
32	47	58	61	56	53	14	3
19	8	55	52	59	64	27	42
46	31	6	17	44	29	4	15
7	18	45	30	5	16	43	28

B

22	25	50	39	52	35	60	57
27	40	23	36	49	58	53	34
24	21	26	51	38	61	56	59
41	28	37	48	3	54	33	62
20	47	42	13	32	63	4	55
29	16	19	46	43	2	7	10
18	45	14	31	12	9	64	5
15	30	17	44	1	6	11	8

C

58	43	60	37	52	41	62	35
49	46	57	42	61	36	53	40
44	59	48	51	38	55	34	63
47	50	45	56	33	64	39	54
22	7	32	1	24	13	18	15
31	2	23	6	19	16	27	12
8	21	4	29	10	25	14	17
3	30	9	20	5	28	11	26

D

50	45	62	41	60	39	54	35
63	42	51	48	53	36	57	38
46	49	44	61	40	59	34	55
43	64	47	52	33	56	37	58
26	5	24	1	20	15	32	11
23	2	27	8	29	12	17	14
6	25	4	21	16	19	10	31
3	22	7	28	9	30	13	18

E

63	22	15	40	1	42	59	18
14	39	64	21	60	17	2	43
37	62	23	16	41	4	19	58
24	13	38	61	20	57	44	3
11	36	25	52	29	46	5	56
26	51	12	33	8	55	30	45
35	10	49	28	53	32	47	6
50	27	34	9	48	7	54	31

F

61	62	63	64	1	2	3	4
60	11	58	57	8	7	54	5
12	59	10	9	56	55	6	53
13	14	15	16	49	50	51	52
20	19	18	17	48	47	46	45
21	38	23	24	41	42	27	44
37	22	39	40	25	26	43	28
36	35	34	33	32	31	30	29

ALPHASQUARE

Set the alphabet (minus Q) in a square of five by five boxes. (Give the players squared paper, and let them do this themselves.) In five minutes, the players must write down all the words they can form, starting anywhere and moving as the chess king does, one square at a time in any direction. The player with the most words wins.

Among the more than two dozen possible words are, for instance, chide, chintz, joints, stun, tunic.

The possibilities become quite different if you write the letters boustrophedon.

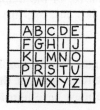

A	B	C	D	E
F	G	H	I	J
K	L	M	N	O
P	R	S	T	U
V	W	X	Y	Z

TARGET WORDS

The problem is to hit the bull's eye.

Have ready—or have each player make—three concentric circles. The second space should be divided into five equal parts, in which you write the five vowels. The outer circle should be divided into ten parts.

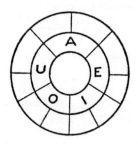

Each player is to think of ten three-letter words that can fit the spaces. They must all end with the same letter, and the second letter must be the appropriate vowel. Possible final letters (for the inner circle) are B, D, G, M, N, P, R, T. The player may write down his ten words, but on another sheet.

On the sheet with the circles, the player writes clues for his ten words. He scrambles the order of the clues. One player may write:

1. because   2. through   3. belongs to a miss   4. evergreen 5. away   6. mutt   7. pointed hill   8. skin for the lady   9. knight 10. vehicle

Players exchange papers. First to fill all the spaces on the target wins. The clues above, in the numbered order, give the words: for, per, her, fir, far, cur, tor, fur, sir, car.

Variation A

Many patterns of Target Words can be devised. Let's try making four concentric circles, and put the vowels in the third from the center. Now we must have four-letter words.

Clues (not in proper order) might be: 1. repair   2. it blows
3. unpopular association   4. popular supply   5. use it to think
with   6. is your word as good as this?   7. makes music   8. des-
patch   9. come to earth   10. tenderly loving. As a further clue,
you may mention that every word has the same letter in the
second circle (this, of course, need not always be the case). The
words indicated by the clues are—mend, wind, bund, fund,
mind, bond, band, send, land, fond.

Variation B

Now try working without putting vowels, or any letters, into
the circles. Make three circles; cut the second into four parts, the
third into eight. These provide hosts of three-letter words; of
course, all must have the same last letter, and each next-to-the-
last letter will be shared by two words. Here are clues for one
such set:

1. senility   2. finality   3. assistance   4. also   5. It helps comfort
me   6. for fishcakes   7. aged   8. offering. As a further clue (in
this case only) you may mention that the second circle holds the
King of Beasts. The words are: eld, end, aid, and, rod ("Thy
rod and thy staff, they comfort me"), cod, old, bid. The King
of Beasts is still the lion.

Variation C

Make four circles, with 16 spaces in the last. Here are clues,
not in consecutive order, for a tricky four-circle Target Game.
Tell the players they can check their work, for if they are right,
the outer circle will remain empty.

Here are the clues: 1. before the foal   2. little fellow   3. ripped
4. thinks he's the boss   5. force   6. impressive volume   7. mimic
8. weed   9. the young lady's as good   10. wag's story   11. and
then some   12. blockhead   13. Irish loudspeaker   14. baked
clay   15. what the receiver does   16. it's money

The answers, in order of the clues, are: mare, tike, tore, male,
make, tome, mime, tare, mile (A miss is as good . . .), tale,

more, mome, mike, tile, take, time. When properly arranged these words repeat around the outer circle *empty* (MT, MT).

CROSS WORDS

Probably no one that can read has escaped seeing a crossword puzzle. For many a person, it is the morning fare on the way to work.

The difficulty of a crossword puzzle depends less on the obscurity of the words than upon the trickiness of the clues. The one I show, with thanks to *The Guardian* (Manchester), traces the desired word through roundabout approaches.

Examine a few of the tricky clues. Seven across is bar row; 16 has *pert* in (inside of) *ent;* 18, "appropriate fuss before exercises," is *ado* before P.T. (for Physical Training); 14 down, "in camera," is an anagram of American. Number 20 puns—low haunts are dives, but Dives is the rich man in the Bible parable of Lazarus (*Luke* 16). The rest I'll leave you the fun of figuring out yourself.

Tricky clues become simpler when you recognize their type. There seem to be four major types. (The number of letters in a word, often apparent from the diagram, is here noted in parenthesis.)

I. *Puns.* Get used to these, and you may bounce along. Thus:

1. jet flier (4)
2. man of the match (10)
3. held up when it rains (8)
4. affords cover for the unmentionable spot, possibly (11)

4. hiding-place (i.e., whipping)
3. umbrella
2. bridegroom
1. crow

II. *Split Words.* The cue mingles the meaning of the word as a whole with the meaning of the parts:

1. Dweller in Manhattan says he runs down (8)
2. The rich widow is all for betting (7)
3. Put the embassy underground for a respite (12)
4. A vehicle is a vehicle is a vehicle (7)

7. drill (Dr. ill)
6. Beat it! (Be at it!)
5. together (to get her)
4. caravan (car a van)
3. intermission (inter mission)

ACROSS

7 Grave forensic dis-
    pute (6).
8 Member of the R. A.
    S. C. or Pioneer
    Corps (8).
9 Four-horsed chariot
    (8).
10 Concomitant perhaps
    of prunes (6).
11 Poser of a sort (5).
12 "My fellow-are
    like Invulnerable
    (Tempest) (9).
14 Proverbially saves
    one over the eight
    (1, 6, 2, 4).
16 Enpertt (9).
18 Appropriate fuss
    before exercises (5).
21 Spread out, as it
    were (6).
22 ... and this is left
    out (8).
23 It may be ours, Evan
    (8).

24 I wager it's a form of
    insect (6).

DOWN

1 Utility oscar for a
    singer (6).
2 Granted I may take
    a rise out of it (8).
3 American novelist's
    double (5).
4 Politician in a pass,
    one worker's in
    agreement (9).
5 A short-lived race ,
    (6).
6 "And honour sinks
    where -- long pre-
    vails" (Goldsmith)
    (8).
8 They bring tears
    to one's eyes (7-6).
13 It should produce a
    weighty harvest
    (9).
14 Foreigner found in
    camera (8).

15 Diligence of study
    in one of these
    Rs (8).
17 The leather worker's

worth? (6).
19 Again it's divided (6).
20 Low haunts for a rich
    man (5)

NOTE-Figures in parentheses denote the number
of letters in the words required.

5. United aim of two men in love with   2. dowager (do wager)
   the same girl (8)   1. islander (I slander)
6. Give up! Don't give up! (6)
7. Bore a practitioner needing a dose
   of his own medicine (5)

SOLUTION

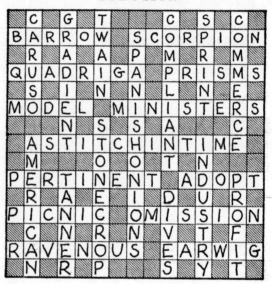

Sometimes the split is simpler, making merely a buried word:

1. Because of rich lu*cre am*nesty was granted.
2. This is a perhaps relatively *unclev*er matter.

III. *Twisted Splits.* The breaking of a word is accompanied
by a pun, or a play that uses pronunciation instead of spelling,
or some other complication:

1. Splitting hairs above the French Riviera (8)
2. Impede the speaker's flank at an empty feast (9)
3. Deal another in a jacket (8)
4. A backward cad, he is first and last a pain above the neck (8)
5. Loll, that is, in short, missing from the undies (6)

1. overnice (over Nice)
2. barmecide (bar m' side)
3. cardigan (card again)
4. headache (*a dac* is a cad backwards; *he* comes at both ends)
5. linger (lingerie minus i.e.—short for that is)

IV. *Anagrams.* The clue includes an anagram of the word:

1. cloth for striptease (10)	6. orchestra
2. Ring a silly girl may wear (4)	5. poetaster
3. Loves to do puzzles (5)	4. insurgent
4. Rebel unresting (9)	3. solve
5. Writer of bad operettas	2. grin
6. Musicians in a carthorse (9)	1. tapestries

Get used to these, and you'll have added fun in your uncrossing or discoursing of crosswords.

Very Cross Words

Numerous outcroppings followed fast upon the popularity of Crosswords. Best known of these is probably Doublecrostic, devised by Elizabeth Seelman Kingsley, and first displayed in the *Saturday Review* of March 31, 1934. In this form, letters from words you must guess go into numbered spaces of a squared pattern, where they form a passage of prose or poetry. And the first letters of the words spell the name of the author and of the quoted work.

The definitions (clues) given for the Doublecrostic are straightforward. Trickier ones are used for the variation called AcrosTickler, devised by Henry Allen and presented first in *The Reporter Magazine* in 1960. Mr. Allen quotes Dryden, saying he has tried to "torture one poor word ten thousand ways." Only the Chinese can boast that many methods of verbal distortion; the AcrosTickler's devices seem to fit in the patterns indicated above.

Thus the clue "Errors sans or sins" gives us the word *errs* (the *or* omitted). "Ant in sys*tem, met*hod and order" has its answer buried. "Ah, it's a poor club that gives one a shut-in feeling" begins with an anagram of claustrophobia.

Slightly Cross Words

Many newspapers have sought a common denominator, offering daily doses of greatly simplified "crossword" guessing games, often with cash awards as circulations builders. "Blackout," "Sweepuzzle," "Pleasure Puzzle," "Quotes," and "Cashword" are some of the names these go by.

The clues for these games are usually simple, and often a list of words, among which are the correct ones, is provided. The trick is that, in from 10 to 20 cases, an unattached letter in the pattern presents multiple choices, among which selection is purely random.

Thus: "A good many letter — are likely to be found in a busy office" (holders, folders). "A — chair is usually designed to be comfortable" (desk, deck). "Persons are not likely to work twenty-four hours without a — " (cause, pause). These defy any hunt for logical preference.

When the paper publishes *The* Solution, it lengthily seeks to justify its choice. (Sometimes there are three, or even four words, offered for your choosing.) Here is one explanation:

"If an employer had to choose between two workers, he might fire the — one." "*Faster* is better. There would be little reason to fire a *fatter* man just because he is fatter; other cause would be necessary. A faster one might sacrifice accuracy to speed and thus be the less desirable employee." Manifestly, the fast man might also be accurate; and the fatter man might consequently be slow or slothful.

The paper often lures subscribers with the thought that they can send in more than one solution, to capture that prize. I asked a mathematics consultant to figure the probability of achieving a perfect score on one puzzle. Because no one had sent in the correct solution in some days, the prize had risen to a tempting

$30,500. The odds for getting all the right words were 1 in 1,040,958,464.

Cross-Rhyme

An interesting variety of fill-in guessing game comes from England. Pairs of clue-words are given; in each pair, one word has a meaning like that of the required word, and the other has a sound like it. Thus, from the pair hint-glue, the required word might be clue. The problem is to find the required words, then to fit them into the crossword boxes. A few letters are put in, to serve as guides. Here are the clue pairs:

love-bird; ermine-coat; brandy-fop; gaff-pole; long-turn; long-lash; sly-rest; hasty-gnash; lessened-caned; pays-customs; clan-gibe; lived-dealt; lunch-champ; wee-insect; dud-boss; concise-nurse; less-muddle; undiluted-suite; yield-deed; stress-praise; dream-vapor; gift-pheasant; stupid-ass; might-battle; slip-traps; firms-conditions

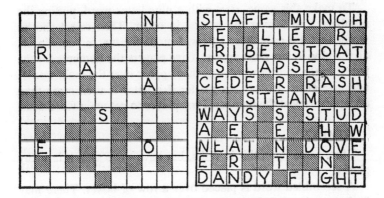

Since I saw but one issue of the now defunct magazine in which this appeared, I had perforce the fun of figuring out the words myself, and fitting them in. They are above, in their places, and here in the order of the clues:

dove, stoat, dandy, staff, yearn, thong, lie, rash, waned, ways, tribe, dwelt, munch, flea, stud, terse, mess, neat, cede, bless, steam, present, crass, fight, lapse, terms

Three simple patterns of word-guessing are fun to make up and try on your friends. They are:

NINERS
This I found in a paper in Essex, England.

Make nine little boxes next to one another, numbered 1 to 9. Or just write the numbers. Solve the clues, and place the letters under the appropriate number. If you are correct, a nine-letter word will appear.   1 2 3 4 5 6 7 8 9

Clues:

Letters 671159 give a golfer's assistant
Letters 3288 give a golf stroke
Letters 3244 give a steady tug   (caddie, putt, pull)   **Put these** under the appropriate numbers, and you have spelled *duplicate*.

To make this game, start with a nine letter word, putting the numbers 1 to 9 over the letters, in order. Then select shorter words that use only those letters. Among the words you choose, all the nine letters must appear. Give players the numbers for the letters in the shorter words (as they appear over the main word), and give clues. It does not matter if a letter is used more than once; just repeat the number. First player to get main word wins.

JUMBLE
I first came upon this in India, but have since seen it in many places.

A scrambled word is placed over a row of boxes. There may be four such words and rows. Problem is to unscramble the anagrams.

Some of the boxes have a circle inside. The letters that belong in these circles will form another anagram ("jumble"), which is sometimes called a "surprise" word or a "mystery personality." Here is a sample Jumble:

```
F E N K I
    O
D C Y N A
    O   O
S O F A L
O O
R H D C O
O       O
```

An after-dinner drink for an old friend.

Unscrambled, the words are knife, candy, loafs (foals would fool you!), chord. The circled letters, unscrambled, yield cordial.

Start with what you will have as your "surprise" word, and you can readily fashion a Jumble.

KNOCK OUT

Here's one I encountered in Hong Kong. It consists of a square of boxes, five by five, with letters in them. More than one letter may be in a box. Clues are provided for four words; each word is formed by letters (or groups of letters) from successive columns. Cross out the letters you use. As the letter you knock out drops from the column, it leaves behind unused ones. The final unused letters can be rearranged to make the "mystery" word. For instance:

```
T   L   AN  E   E
R   O   IN  G   D
H   NG  R   E   R
ST  O   P   AN  B
E   R   L   S   ER
```

Clues	Words
1. not killed by the automobile	4. toper
2. "I have been a —— in a strange land."	3. England
3. There'll always be an . . .	2. stranger
4. imbiber	1. horse

The letters left, rearranged, make the music man (and city) Berlin.

To make Knock Out for a party is simple. Take or make a square of 25 boxes. Fit four words into the top four rows, putting two letters into one column, if necessary. In the same way, fit the name of a well-known person into the fifth row. Or you may use the name of someone expected at the party.

Now scramble the letters of that name, by shuffling them into different columns.

Write clues for the four words.

Now mix up all the units within each column, by shifting letters or groups (keep each group as a unit) up and down. Do not change from column to column.

You are now ready to play. Make enough copies for the guests; or give them sheets of squared paper and dictate the letters and the clues. The first to get all the words and the name, wins.

The best workers with crosswords are themselves seldom cross.

9

Relatively Game

Of the hundreds of games linked with persons and places and names, only a culling is offered here. We trust they give play for power.

KIN GAME

We all know, since Wycherley, Swift and Scott passed on the word from Plato, that necessity is the mother of invention. Fewer are aware that laziness is the father of the minx.

How many other relatives can you name? Ask your friends to set down all they can in three minutes. Here are a few:

Wealth is the father of luxury and indolence, poverty of meanness and viciousness, and both of discontent   (*Plato*)
Soot, brother of flickering fire   (*Aeschylus*)
Athens, mother of arts and eloquence   (*Milton*)
England is the mother of Parliaments   (*John Bright*)
Natural philosophy, great mother of the sciences   (*Francis Bacon*)
Urine, the soft-flowing daughter of Fright   (*Coleridge*)
Sleep, brother of death   (*Sir Thomas Browne, Samuel Daniel, etc.*)

Nothing! Thou elder brother even to shade   (*John Wilmot, Earl of Rochester*)
(of Night): Thy brother Death came and cried . . .
Thy sweet child Sleep, the dreamy-eyed   (*Shelley*)
O father of us all, Paian Apollo!   (*Swinburne*)
The child is father of the man   (*Wordsworth*)
Thy wish was father, Harry, to the thought   (*Shakespeare*)
Experience is the child of thought, and thought is the child of action   (*Disraeli*)
Fashion, though Folly's child, and guide of fools . . .   (*George Crabbe*)
(the Cloud) I am the daughter of Earth and Water   (*Shelley*)
(of Venice): Sun-girt city, thou hast been
Ocean's child . . .   (*Shelley*)
Perfection is the child of time.   (*Bishop Joseph Hall*)
Sweetest Shakespeare, Fancy's child   (*Milton*)
Carnage (so Wordsworth tells you) is God's daughter.   (*Byron*)
Devotion, daughter of Astronomy! An undevout astronomer is mad.   (*Edward Young*)
O daughter of Death and Priapus, Our Lady of Pain   (*Swinburne*)
(of Adversity): Daughter of Jove, relentless power,
Thou tamer of the human breast.   (*Thomas Gray*)
The owl always believes that his son is a hawk.   (*Hungarian proverb*)

NAME WORDS

Many of our English words are made from names. Allow five minutes for the players to write as many words as they can, derived from names of places or persons—historical, mythical, or fictional.

The one with most words wins BUT he must be able to identify the origin of the word.

Variation

Make up sentences, each using a word derived from a name. Then remove that word, and substitute another word or expression with the same meaning.

Dictate these sentences. Players must substitute the word that comes from a name. First to get them all wins. Here are some samples:

1. The eruption of a molten mountain destroyed Pompeii.	10. martial
2. The ground was covered with snow for most of the month.	9. hamburger
3. His tremendous heave lifted the massy rock.	8. tantalizing
4. Timothy felt like a wealthy man as he sat back in the Rolls Royce.	7. terpsichorean
5. The man reached his destination after a 4,000 mile journey.	6. cereals
6. In most countries the main food supply is from grains.	5. odyssey
7. The young man felt that he would never attain skill in the dancing art.	4. plutocrat
8. It was a teasing spread of delicious food he was forbidden to eat.	3. herculean
9. All he could eat was a broiled patty of chopped meat.	2. March or January
10. They were all stirred by the military strains of the music.	1. volcano

Here are just a few of the multitudinous flow of words from names:

kilowatt, lynch, boycott, frankfurter, arras, atlas, aphrodisiac, argosy, ammonia, pickwickian, quixotic, diesel, angstrom, volt, calico, pants, denim, hackneyed, sandwich, bedlam, afghan, coolie, copper, dollar, alchemy, alabaster, arabesque, hermaphrodite, colt, jockey, polka, gun, spinach, spaniel, valentine, agaric, agate, ampere, artesian, babbitt, bacchanals, battology, bayonet, begonia, blanket, bloomers, bohemian, bowdlerize, braille, brie, bronze, camellia, camembert, caryatid, coach, cologne, cravat, cupidity, currant, dauphin, derby, doily, echo, epicurean, ermine, euphuistic, fez, frieze, galvanize, gardenia, gargantuan, guillotine, hector, helot, hermetically, hyacinth, indigo, iris, jeremiad, jovial, laconic, lilliputian, lyceum, magnet, martinet, maudlin, mausoleum, mayonnaise, mentor, mercurial, milliner, mnemonic, morphine, nicotine, ogre, ohm, panic, parchment, pasteurize, peach, praline, procrustean, protean, prussic, quisling, rhinestone, samaritan, sardine, sardonic, satire, saturnine, saxophone, shanghai, shrapnel, silhouette, sequoia, solecism, spruce, stentorian, sybarite, tangerine, titanic, tobacco, vaudeville, venereal, vulcanize.

CITY-ZEN

The old philosophy of the East has invaded the cities of the West. With a wry twist. With ham. Mainly it's made-up, new style.

Try to see—allow players to see how many cities they can make up, in three minutes, that fit the state they put them in. (Don't let it get you in a state!) Give an example. Players decide which are cleverest. Thus you may have:

Tinn Kan; Tellme Wyo; Wet Wash; Dothe Minn; Hittor Miss; Infi Del; Pigg Penn; Proand Conn; Either Ore; Sitbees Ida; Betchai Kan; Latch Ky; Under Pa; Noahs Ark; Mapleb Ark; Hoop La; Marry Me; Misery Me; Farmerinthe Del; Aspho Del; Matad Ore; Neverm Ore; Dinos Ore; Count Tenn; Valh Ala; Trustin Ala; Bringthe Minn; Catchascatch Kan; Critical Mass; Pantomai Md; Justa Mo; Dafford Ill; Pianissi Mo; Versat Ill; Imbes Ill; Lo Cal; Vita Minn. Do go on!

NAMES GAMES

Of the familiar authors whose works may be rifled for quiz games, only three will here be drawn upon, by way of illustration. A book has been devoted to quizzes on Shakespeare alone. Here is just one:

Shakespeare

From the plays, or any book of quotations, select a few brief passages. Read them aloud, stopping after each for the players to write the name of the play, and the character that speaks the words. Have the answers read aloud. Score two for correct play, five for correct character. Highest score wins.

Here are a few to start you off:

1. Many a time and oft In the Rialto you have rated me About my monies and my usances.
2. Men are April when they woo, December when they wed.
3. The fault, dear Brutus, is not in our stars, but in ourselves, that we are underlings.
4. She hangs upon the cheek of night like a rich jewel in an Ethiop's ear.
5. She speaks poniards, and every word stabs.
6. Things bad begun make strong themselves by ill.
7. Thou wouldst as soon go kindle fire with snow as seek to quench the fire of love with words.
8. Thus conscience does make cowards of us all.
9. And as the sun breaks through the darkest clouds, so honour peereth in the meanest habit.
10. To be honest, as this world goes, is to be one man picked out of ten thousand.
11. Well said! That was laid on with a trowel.

1. The Merchant of Venice; Shylock
2. As You Like It; Rosalind
3. Julius Caesar; Cassius
4. Romeo and Juliet; Romeo
5. Much Ado About Nothing; Benedick
6. Macbeth; Macbeth
7. The Two Gentlemen of Verona; Julia
8. Hamlet; Hamlet
9. The Taming of the Shrew; Petruchio
10. Hamlet; Hamlet
11. As You Like It; Celia

Dickens

Before the decline of Dickens, he was a frequent subject of the literary quiz. Today he is so neglected that the wide-ranging *Literature and Western Man,* by J. B. Priestley (March, 1960), though the text dutifully declares of the mid-nineteenth century that "the two greatest novelists of this age are Tolstoy and Dickens," omits Dickens from the 124 biographies of writers at the end.

Dated Cambridge, 1857, is a quiz on "The Posthumous Papers of the Pickwick Club" from which I reclaim five questions:

1. Mention any occasions on which it is specified that the Fat Boy was *not* asleep; and that (1) Mr. Pickwick and (2) Mr. Weller, Senr., ran. Deduce from expressions used on one occasion Mr. Pickwick's maximum of speed.
4. What operation was performed on Tom Smart's chair? Who little thinks that in which pocket, of what garment, in where, he has left what, entreating him to return to whom, with how many what, and all how big?
8. Give in full Samuel Weller's first compliment to Mary, and his father's critique upon the same young lady. What church was on the valentine that first attracted Mr. Samuel's eye in the shop?
19. What is a red-faced Nixon?
30. Who, besides Mr. Pickwick, is recorded to have worn gaiters?

Question 19 came a century before any American political pertinence. Dickens was referring to Robert Nixon, the Cheshire prophet, whose forecasts were published as chapbooks. Was he red-faced merely on a chapbook cover, or because his prophesies proved false?

Gilbert and Sullivan

Lovers of lighter fare still turn to the merriest minglers of music and words after Aristophanes. Time was when at the broach of a Gilbertian line, I could give you the rest of the speech.

In those days, I knew the answers to the test given in an article of mine on the peerless pair (printed in *The Drama* of December, 1925). It draws upon the Bab Ballads as well as the comic operas. Here it is, for old fogies like myself who still cherish Gilbert and Sullivan.

1. Write a brief essay on Gilbert's use of chops or mutton-chops (he did not mean meat), with reference to at least two operas and three Bab Ballads.

2. Draw up a table to show when Frederick was born. Do you consider that Gilbert forgot that 1900 would not be a leap year? If you do, why do you?

3. List anecdotes from the Bab Ballads about colonial bishops, and quote from an opera a description of their diocesan atmosphere.

4. Which chorus has at least one grandparent living? On the authority of what statement?

5. Quote from two operas, for each of the following:
    a. references to oil at different temperatures;
    b. stage directions for the display of indifference.

6. Who was rather dressy for her age, and what was her age?

7. Describe in Gilbert's words two A's, three B's, two C's, D's, E's, F's, and one G. How does the list of these differ from someone in another opera, who was said to have been seen doing what with whom on the what of the what?

8. Identify:
    a. a man all poetry and buzzem;
    b. a quiet venerable duck;
    c. Popsy;
    d. the man who had the run of the royal rum;
    e. the man who drove a Putney bus (give full name, and creed).

9. Who, in which opera, married his nurse? What was his Christian name, and how do you know it?

10. The following phrases occur each in two operas. Give references or quote context to identify them:
    a. matrimonified
    b. Monday Pops
    c. shrivel into raisins
    d. despite his best endeavour
    e. each a little bit afraid is
    f. miminy-piminy
    g. ladies' seminary (give all words rhyming with seminary in both operas)

11. Explain, with references:
    a. Basingstoke

   b. Burglaree
   c. a descendant by purchase
   d. that's so like a band
   e. Mr. Wilkinson
   f. Warren
   g. Stephen Trusty
   h. Gideon Crawle
   i. the dancing catalog of crime
12. Give eight pairs of forced rhyme for one opera. Where is the only metrical error in any opera? Quote the best two examples, in all the works, of common phrases introduced rhythmically.

It seems appropriate, in a book of word wonder, to add Gilbert's discussion of the greatest riddle of all:

> Try we life-long, we can never
> Straighten out life's tangled skein,
> Why should we, with vain endeavor,
> Guess and guess and guess again?
> Life's a pudding full of plums;
> Care's a canker that benumbs.
> Wherefore waste our elocution
> On impossible solution:
> Life's a pleasant institution—
> Let us take it as it comes.

> Set aside the dull enigma,
> We shall guess it all too soon;
> Failure brings no kind of stigma—
> Dance we to another tune.
> String the lyre and fill the cup,
> Lest on sorrow we should sup.
> Hop and skip to Fancy's fiddle,
> Hands across and down the middle—
> Life's perhaps the only riddle
> That we shrink from giving up.

10

Pied and Pickled Proverbs

What shall we do with the shrunken proverb? For indeed the wise saw has grown rusty. No longer, as with Cervantes and Mark Twain or George Ade, is the aid of an adage, an aphorism, a maxim, a gnome, an apothegm, apophthegm, a saying, a mot, a phylactery, or even a wheeze on the tip of every tongue. And with their lapse has gone much of the color and power of our speech.

Let us seek to revive them. Let us play with proverbs.

PROVERBUILD

One player goes out of the room. The rest select a saying, and one word or group of words in the saying is assigned to each person in the room. Every word should be assigned, and every player should have an assignment.

The lone player returns. He may question the players in any order. They must answer his questions (as directly or oddly as they desire) AND in every answer they must use their assigned word. (If two words were assigned one player, they must be words next to one another in the saying, and he must use them that way in his answer.)

The object is to guess the saying as quickly as possible. When it is guessed, another player goes out, and the process is repeated.

When all have had a chance, the one that guessed most quickly is the winner.

Answers can be tricky. If a player has a word like "hesitates," he should try to divert attention from it by some other expression, like "over the moon" or "has its day," that will suggest another saying and confuse the guesser.

VOWEL OUT

Omit all the vowels in a saying. Write it, running all the consonants together.

Here is a fairly easy one, because it's always the same vowel that you add. This inscription is cut in stone, on a church in Wales, over the Ten Commandments:

1. prsvryprfctmn
   vrkpthsprcptstn

In the examples of proverbs that follow, different vowels are out:

2. glsssndlsssrbrttlwr
3. tstlttsprwhnthbttmsbr
4. ncststhmthrfnvntn

Dictate the letters of a vowel-out saying. If no one can get it in a reasonable time, give a clue. The first clue is to tell how many words there are in the expression. If this doesn't help, give a clue to the idea. Here are clues to the four above:

1. Be at ease. If this doesn't help, say the only missing letter is *e*.
2. Girls are fragile creatures.
3. Too little not in time.
4. When you must you can.

The sayings themselves are:

1. Persevere ye perfect men,
   Ever keep these precepts ten.
2. Glasses and lasses are brittle ware.
3. It is too late to spare when the bottom is bare.
4. Necessity is the mother of invention.

PROVERGRAMS

Scramble separately each word in a saying. Then change the order of the scrambled words.

Dictate these scrambles to the players. The one that gets most proverbs right (or gets them all first) wins. Here are three samples:

brutte srowd srapspin on nefi.
hent dan kapes sfirt kniht.
medoferra drenweroaf.

Here, in a different order, are the three sayings:

Think first and then speak.
Forewarned, forearmed.
Fine words butter no parsnips.

Variation

Mix the whole proverb in one long scramble. Dictate this, telling the players how many words are in the saying. The simplest scramble is to put all the letters alphabetically. For instance:

aaeegghillmnnnnoooorrssssstt (6 words)
aaceeeffhhiiiiimnnnoooprrsstttt (6 words)
aabdeeeeeffffhiiikmnnnrrsst (5 words)

If necessary, after a few minutes give a clue. For these three:

Don't go rambling around.
Do it now.
Dress up fit to kill.

You will recognize the sayings:

A rolling stone gathers no moss.
Procrastination is the thief of time.
Fine feathers make fine birds.

Turn a Phrase

Some sayings permit pleasant perversion. We all know, for example, that familiarity breeds contempt. Fewer have advanced to observe that familiarity breeds contemplation. More might agree that familiarity breeds children.

Any farmer will tell you that a straw shows which way the wind blows. Politicians and pollsters are less likely to admit that a straw vote shows which way the hot air blows.

Some co-eds pursue learning, some learn pursuing.

Most persons know by now that he who laughs last has no sense of humor.

Give your literate companions a few such examples—and three minutes to make up some themselves. The group decides which are cleverest.

Few persons know the sources of familiar sayings, although many of them had origin in the words or the works of an identified man. But you may see how well informed your friends are. Dictate a saying; allow 45 seconds for players to write the source. Then give another. I set a few below; most books of proverbs and sayings will give you the authors as well.

1. in the nick o' time	10.	Bible (Psalms)
2. There's a daisy!	9.	Shakespeare
3. Care will kill a cat.	8.	Shakespeare
4. She's no chicken.	7.	Rabelais
5. He went away with a flea in his ear.	6.	Michael Drayton
6. The coast was clear.	5.	John Fletcher
7. Let us fly and save our bacon.	4	Jonathan Swift
8. I have you on the hip.	3.	George Wither
9. I cannot tell what the dickens his name was.	2.	Shakespeare
10. at their wit's end	1.	John Suckling

Here, in final measure, comes a gathering of sayings and saws, which can be read for the felicitous phrasing of a searching thought, or for use in many of the games in this book. These, again, are but a meager culling from the thousands men in their time have made.

1. Whilst Adam slept, Eve from his side arose:
   Strange his first sleep should be his last repose.

2. That's a very mean animal—when attacked, it defends itself.
3. Who would not look on a fool must smash his mirror.
4. One cloud is enough to hide the sun.
5. He that is giddy thinks the world turns round.
6. The wheel that does the squeaking gets the grease.
7. Every sprat nowadays calls itself a herring.
8. The edge of plenty is better than the very middle of want.
9. An end will come to the world, but music and love will endure.
10. If I rest, I rust.
11. When I was frightened I threatened others.
12. A good bird begins chirping in the egg.
13. It is the grace of lambs to suckle kneeling.
14. However far a bird may fly, it takes its tail along.
15. He runs well, but he is off the track.
16. A kiss without a moustache is like an egg without salt.
17. In the distant field the cabbages are fine.
18. I have no chickens and no quarrel with the fox.
19. For the lucky one, even his rooster lays.
20. A bald head is soon shaven.
21. A barleycorn is better than a diamond, to a hen.
22. Accuracy is a duty, not a virtue.
23. A bad custom's like a good cake: better broken.
24. Never had bad workman good tools.
25. A candle lights others and consumes itself.
26. Lazy as Ludlam's dog, that leaned against the wall to bark.
27. Bachelors' wives (and maids' children) are well taught.
28. No rope is strong enough to hang the truth.
29. "A great squeal for a little wool!" exclaimed the man as he sheared the pig.
30. He that relies too much on himself has a fool for a master.
31. If you don't know where you are going, any road will take you there.
32. Foul water as soon as fair will quench hot fire.
33. Through a small hole one can see the sky.
34. There never was a good town but had a mire at one end.
35. Jack would be a gentleman if he could speak French.
36. Wit is brushwood; judgment, timber.
37. It is of no use running; set out on time.

38. One must not laugh at one's own wheeze;
    A snuff-box has no right to sneeze.
39. Great souls have wills; feeble ones, only wishes.
40. All are not thieves that dogs bark at.
41. A black hen lays a white egg.
42. A blind man will not thank you for a looking-glass.
43. A maid that laughs is half ta'en.
44. A man cannot whistle and drink at the same time.
45. A straight stick is crooked in the water.
46. A young man should not marry yet, an old man not at all.
47. All things are difficult before they are easy.
48. Beware of the man of one book.
49. By the street of By and By one arrives at the house of Never.
50. Danger and delight grow on one stock.
51. Sowed cockle reaps no corn.
52. When the cook has spoiled the food, the flute player will be beaten.
53. Envy shoots at others and wounds herself.
54. Every ass loves to hear himself bray.
55. Every man can tame a shrew but he who has her.
56. Give a lie twenty-four hours' start, and you can never overtake it.
57. Good and quickly seldom meet.
58. He cannot speak well that cannot hold his tongue.
59. He is a fool that is not melancholy once a day.
60. He never lies but when the holly is green.
61. He that does you an ill turn will never forgive you.
62. He that will eat the kernel must crack the nut.
63. He that wipes the child's nose kisses the mother's lips.
64. He was a bold man that first ate an oyster.
65. An agreeable person is one that agrees with me.
66. He was a man of one idea—and that was wrong.
67. Silence is deep as eternity, speech is as shallow as time.
68. France was long a despotism tempered by epigrams.
69. Do not speak disrespectfully of the Equator!
70. We are all on our last cruise.
71. 'Tis very warm weather when one's in bed.
72. A cucumber should be well sliced, and dressed with pepper and vinegar, and thrown out.

73. "I did that," says my memory. "I could not have done that," says my pride. Eventually memory yields.
74. We are all in the gutter, but some of us are looking at the stars.
75. Sow an act, and you reap a habit. Sow a habit, and you reap a character. Sow a character, and you reap a destiny.
76. God cannot alter the past; historians can.
77. Life is the art of drawing sufficient conclusions from insufficient premises.
78. To live is like love: all reason is against it, but all healthy instinct for it.
79. There's many a good tune played on an old fiddle.
80. I wish he would explain his explanation.
81. In England there are sixty religions, and one sauce.
82. Justice is truth in action.
83. Hope is as inexpensive as despair.
84. Hypocrisy is the homage vice pays to virtue.
85. He can see as far into a millstone as another.
86. If all fools wore white caps we'd seem a flock of geese.
87. If all men say thou art an ass, bray.
88. If the beard were all, the goat might preach.
89. In every country the sun rises in the morning.
90. In the grave, dust and bones jostle not for the wall.
91. It is not how long, but how well, we live.
92. Keep your eyes wide open before marriage and half-shut afterwards.
93. Lean liberty is better than fat slavery.
94. Learning makes a good man better and an ill man worse.
95. Living well is the best revenge.
96. Keep some till more come.
97. Many would be cowards if they had courage enough.
98. More belongs to marriage than four bare legs in a bed.
99. Music helps not the toothache.
100. No churchyard is so handsome that a man would desire straight to be buried there.
101. No sweet without sweat.
102. Old men and travelers may lie by authority.
103. You cannot make an omelet without breaking eggs.
104. One hair of a woman draws more than a team of oxen.

105. Our last garment is made without pockets. (How much neater, this, than the crude "You can't take it with you"!)
106. Punctuality is the politeness of princes.
107. Riches are like muck, which stink in a heap, but spread abroad make the earth fruitful.
108. Say to pleasure—"Gentle Eve, I will none of your apple."
109. Scald not your lips in another man's pottage.
110. Sport is sweetest when there are no spectators.
111. Step after step the ladder is climbed.
112. The absent are always in the wrong.
113. The boughs that bear most hang lowest.
114. The busiest men have the most leisure.
115. The evils hardest to bear are the ones we bring on ourselves.
116. The fly sat on the hub of the wheel and said—"What a dust I raise!"
117. The higher the ape goes, the more he shows his tail.
118. The moon does not heed the barking of the dogs.
119. The prodigal robs his heir; the miser, himself.
120. The heat that melts the wax will harden the clay.
121. The soul is not where it lives, but where it loves.
122. The sun is never the worse for shining on a dunghill.
123. There is no pack of cards without a knave.
124. Don't dig your grave with your teeth.
125. Two things a man should never be angry at—what he can help, and what he cannot help.
126. Wanton kittens may make sober cats.
127. When a friend asks, there is no tomorrow.
128. When the sun is highest he casts the least shadow.
129. When you can tread on nine daisies at once, spring has come.
130. While the tall maid is stooping, the little one hath swept the house.
131. Who will not be ruled by the rudder must be ruled by the rock.
132. Willows are weak, yet they bind other wood.
133. Wise men learn by other men's mistakes; fools, by their own.
134. Not all trees have the same bark.
135. Open the window, light and God stream in!

136. Worry is rust upon the blade.
137. I cannot draw a cart, nor eat dried oats; but if it is man's work I will do it.
138. By night an atheist half believes in God.
139. It is hard for an empty bag to stand upright.
140. We seldom repent having eaten too little.
141. Four boxes rule the world—cartridge-box, ballot-box, jury-box, and band-box.
142. Not Hercules could have knocked his brains out, for he had none.
143. Calamity is man's true touchstone.
144. Use every man after his deserts, and who shall 'scape whipping?
145. The owner should be an ornament to the house, not the house to the owner.
146. Idleness travels slowly, and poverty soon overtakes her.
147. Necessity is the tyrant's plea.
148. An extraordinary haste to discharge an obligation is a sort of ingratitude.
149. Perseverance comes from a strong will, obstinacy from a strong won't.
150. It is not poverty so much as pretense that harasses a man.
151. Who will not reason, is a bigot; who cannot, is a fool; who dares not, is a slave.
152. When a man has no good reason for doing a thing, he has one good reason for letting it alone.
153. Let us be silent, that we may hear the whispers of the gods.
154. A small leak will sink a great ship.
155. What ardently we wish we soon believe.
156. Women's styles may change, but their designs remain the same.
157. Don't listen to one and judge two.
158. A wonder lasts nine days; a miracle, ten.
159. Fiddle-de-dee and pine nuts, and perforated spoons.
160. Good food, good meat,
Good God, let's eat!
161. Pull the child out of the water before you punish it.
162. Even if you sit on the bottom of the sea, you cannot be a fish.
163. No man is clever enough to lick his own back.

164. Scatter ashes, and the wind will blow them in your eyes.
165. The debt to breeze and moonlight can never be repaid.
166. Hurt is the price we pay for feeling.
167. Is your bottle half full, or half empty?
168. It sure is dark if you shut your eyes.
169. What is past, is prologue.
170. That butterfly was a caterpillar; that dust was a butterfly.
171. Sticks are thrown only at trees that grow fruit.
172. Do not fall in love; rise to it!
173. Do it now, and you can spell *now* backwards.
174. Take your job seriously, but not yourself.
175. The biggest fool is a learned fool.
176. Happiness was born a twin.
177. Don't fell the tree to catch the bird.
178. Every cock is proud of his own dunghill.
179. Every word was once a poem.
180. Who cuts his own wood warms himself twice.
181. Habit turns a cobweb into a cable.
182. Nothing should ever be done for the first time.
183. He lards his lean books with the fat of others' labors.
184. When the son swore Diogenes struck the father.
185. The cleverest ruse of the Devil is to persuade us he doesn't exist.
186. 'Tis always morning somewhere in the world.
187. A weed is a flower in disguise.
188. It will all be one a hundred years hence.
189. The reward of a thing well done, is to have done it.
190. If we walk in the woods, we must feed mosquitos.
191. All that is needed for scientific research is running water and an idea.
192. L'art, c'est moi; la science, c'est nous.
193. The dragon is the most cosmopolitan of impossibilities.
194. The checkmate in chess symbolizes patricide by castration.
195. The art of pleasing consists in being pleased.
196. We never do anything well until we stop thinking about how to do it.
197. War makes rattling good history, but peace is poor reading.
198. His thoughts are as slow as a lone cave's stillicide.
199. Everything passes, everything perishes, everything palls.
200. Ole Man Know-All died last year.

201. Youk'n hide de fier, but w'at you gwine do wid de smoke?
202. Thousands kiss the outside that never look within.
203. She was five minutes late all her life.
204. When you have nothing to say, take less than fifteen minutes.
205. I am always of the opinion of the learned, if they speak first.
206. The virtue that must be ever guarded is scarce worth the sentinel.
207. This is pretty, but I don't know what it means.
208. Woman is one of nature's most agreeable blunders.
209. It is better not to know so much than to know so much that isn't so.
210. Most conversation is but ceremonial gesture.
211. Winter and wedlock tames man and beast.
212. There is a day of judgment for the orator as well as the deceased.
213. Manners are the happy way of doing things.
214. As I would not be a slave, so I would not be a master.
215. The axis of the earth sticks out visibly through the center of every town.
216. Any man can be in good spirits when he's well dressed.
217. It is usually easier to suppress criticism than to meet it.
218. The learned man knows the rules, the wise man knows the exceptions.
219. Make your manner worthy of your mind.
220. This is my opinion, and I share it.
221. A carefree head is found only on a scarecrow.
222. A good companion shortens the longest road.
223. A heart in love with beauty never grows old.
224. Patience is bitter, but it bears sweet fruit.
225. Though the chimney be crooked, smoke will rise straight.
226. Who speaks evil to you will speak evil of you.
227. You can't make a stallion out of a donkey by clipping its ears.
228. Beware of all enterprises that require new clothes.
229. Take your time; your mother waited till you were born.
230. Instead of denying the light, scrape the dust off your window.
231. I hate quotations. Tell me what you know.
     Ergo sum.

Index